Programming for
Microprocessors

Programming for Microprocessors

ANDREW COLIN MA, FBCS, CEng, FIEE

Professor of Computer Science,
University of Strathclyde, Scotland

NEWNES – BUTTERWORTHS
LONDON   BOSTON
Sydney   Wellington   Durban   Toronto

The Butterworth Group

United Kingdom **Butterworth & Co (Publishers) Ltd**
London: 88 Kingsway, WC2B 6AB

Australia **Butterworths Pty Ltd**
Sydney: 586 Pacific Highway, Chatswood, NSW 2067
Also at Melbourne, Brisbane, Adelaide and Perth

Canada Butterworth & Co (Canada) Ltd
Toronto: 2265 Midland Avenue, Scarborough, Ontario
M1P 4S1

New Zealand **Butterworths of New Zealand Ltd**
Wellington: T & W Young Building, 77–85 Customhouse
Quay, 1, CPO Box 472

South Africa **Butterworth & Co (South Africa) (Pty) Ltd**
Durban: 152–154 Gale Street

USA **Butterworth (Publishers) Inc**
Boston: 19 Cummings Park, Woburn, Mass. 01801

First published 1979

© Butterworth & Co (Publishers) Ltd, 1979

British Library Cataloguing in Publication Data

Colin, Andrew John Theodore
    Programming for microprocessors.
    1. Microprocessors—Programming
    I. Title
    001.6'42   QA76.6   78-40694

    ISBN 0-408-00320-0

Typeset by Reproduction Drawings Ltd., Sutton, Surrey
Printed in England by Cox & Wyman Ltd, London,
Fakenham and Reading

Preface

Microprocessors are at the confluence of two major engineering traditions—electronics and computer science. Most intending users of microprocessors already have a broad background in one or other of these areas, so the author of a general book on microprocessors would have to accept that many of his readers already knew half of what he had to say.

This book avoids the problem by assuming that its readers start with some knowledge of digital electronics. Computer scientists who have never studied the properties of electronic hardware will find the text difficult in places.

A useful and satisfying way of writing a book is to present a subject in broad, simplified terms, ignoring details and concentrating on the larger issues. Unfortunately, a book on microprocessors written in this style would leave the reader very little the wiser; in microprocessing the details are as important as more general decisions. If you make the mistake of choosing the wrong microprocessor, your system will be a little slower and more expensive than if you had made the best choice; but if the details of your program or data representation are wrong, your system will not work at all. No apology, therefore, is required for those chapters that descend to the finest level of detail: they are a necessary part of the book.

Matters of detail are hard to appreciate, particularly in the abstract. This book is not designed to be read straight through and fully absorbed. Instead, the reader is invited to skim the more difficult chapters, at least at the first reading, and then to return and study them carefully only when there arises a practical need to do so. Features that seem difficult and obscure when seen out of context tend to become quite straightforward when actually used for a particular purpose.

It is widely accepted that it is next to impossible to guarantee the correctness of computer programs. The programs in this book have all either been run or—where that was not practicable—checked carefully by two persons. This does not guarantee that they are right; indeed, it is highly probable that several mistakes remain.

One of the high-level languages chosen for discussion is PL/F, which was designed by Fergus Duncan, then a Research Student at Strathclyde University. The definition of this language is quoted in full in Appendix 3, and I am indebted to its author for permission to use it.

My thanks are due to Miss Agnes Wisley, who typed the manuscript; to Mr. Duncan Smeed, who helped to check the programs; to the members of two extension studies evening classes who acted as 'guinea-pigs' for a preliminary draft of the book; and lastly to my wife, family and publishers, who severally encouraged me to complete the text.

A. J. T. C.

Contents

General introduction

The microprocessor

Many major advances in human knowledge have resulted from the cross-fertilisation of two different disciplines. One product of such a union is the microprocessor, which represents the flowering both of electronics and of computer science.

The microprocessor brings a new dimension of freedom, capability and power to both areas. The electronic engineer can now design control and signal-processing systems of unparalleled reliability, speed and simplicity, while the computer scientist can obtain as much computer power as he needs at a small fraction of its previous cost.

The mixed parentage of the microprocessor gives it two entirely different aspects, each of which tells only part of the truth. An engineer schooled in conventional electronics might think of it as the culmination of a line of digital components starting with elementary logic gates, and including registers, adders, arithmetic units and stores. This view is correct as far as it goes, but fails to take into account the 'computer' dimension of the microprocessor. An engineer who saw the device solely as an electronic component would not be able to put it to effective use.

The other aspect of the microprocessor is seen by the computer scientist. When he first reads a description, the computer scientist can see no essential difference between the structure of the microprocessor and the large mainframes or minicomputers he has been using hitherto. It has basically the same arrangement of store, arithmetic and control units, and it is clear that all the programming techniques and tools such as assemblers, editors and high-level languages are as applicable to microprocessors as they are to conventional computers. The main stumbling block to the computer scientist is that the microprocessor is only a component, and to be of any use it must be built into a complete system with other components. This severely practical point has so far prevented some computer scientists from taking a serious interest in microprocessors.

It appears, then, that to make full use of microprocessors the system designer must be grounded both in electronics and in computer science subjects that traditionally cover different areas. Unlike computer scientists, electronic engineers have shown a great deal of enthusiasm for the new development; but they have often encountered great difficulties because of their inexperience in the techniques of computer science. To the computer specialist's eye, engineers often painfully re-invent methods that were fully understood 20 years ago.

The present writer is a computer scientist with some knowledge of digital electronics. This book attempts to bridge the crevasse between these two subjects, by starting from the side of the engineer, taking for granted a basic knowledge of digital electronics and concentrating on the computer-like aspects of microprocessors.

Hardwired and programmed systems

The basic feature that makes a microprocessor more than just a component is its generality, and its ability to switch between several different functions within a few microseconds.

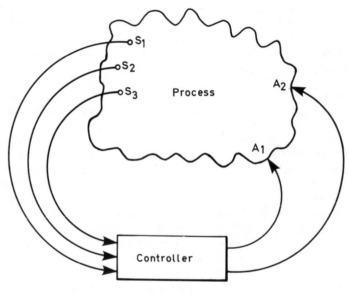

Figure 1.1

Consider a digital controller for a chemical process (*Figure 1.1*). Sensors S_1, S_2 and S_3 supply essential information about temperatures, pressures, flow rates and so on. Actuators A_1 and A_2 control valve settings and motor speeds so as to keep the process running at the right conditions for the best yield. The controller may also double as a 'safety device', shutting down the entire process or opening a relief valve if one of the sensors reports a value that exceeds some predetermined mean.

In the past, a controller of this type could well have been built using traditional components such as relays or elementary logic gates. The inputs would have been converted from analogue to digital form by A/D converters, and the outputs would have been handled by D/A converters whenever necessary. This type of construction is called 'hardwired', because the control function is totally embodied in the components and their connections. A common feature of a hardwired design is that every aspect of a specification is translated directly into its own assembly of components. Thus a safety requirement involving five inputs would be implemented by five connected relays or a five-input logic network.

Today, the same control function can be provided by a microprocessor. The controller still has the same connections to the system being controlled, and the signals must still be converted to and from the digital form; but the internal arrangement is now totally different. Instead of many components each dedicated to a specific purpose, the system has only a few parts; but they are configured so that they can carry out all the necessary functions one after the other in sequence. When the system has executed all the control functions once, it loops back and executes them again, and so on continuously. Each control function can be executed every few milliseconds, giving a close approximation to continuous control.

The information governing the control functions is stored as a series of 'instructions' in a store attached to the control system. As soon as it has finished executing any one function, the system fetches the instructions governing the next function from this store. A typical set of control instructions might carry the meaning:

1. If temperature $> 250°$ ring alarm
2. If pressure > 50 kg/cm^2 ring alarm
3. If flow > 102 litre/s close inlet valve one step
4. If flow < 98 litre/s open valve one step

19. Wait 2 seconds
20. Go back to step 1

It should be noted that the actual form in which the instructions are stored is considerably different from the one shown above; the intention, however, is the same.

Figure 1.2 shows the internal structure of a control system based on a microprocessor. A vital feature of this structure is that it is the *same* for any controller. Different control functions can be obtained simply by changing the instructions held in the store. In the limit a microprocessor can implement any control function, no matter how complex.

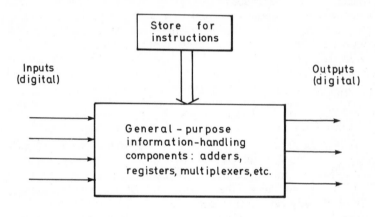

Figure 1.2

The only condition is that the function be capable of complete and unambiguous definition.

The set of instructions that produces any control function is called a 'program'. A microprocessor is therefore often referred to as a 'programmed' device, to distinguish it from one that is hardwired.

Some contrasting properties of hardwired and programmed devices

It is worth comparing hardwired and programmed systems, since they differ in several important ways.

Complexity of control

One measure of control function is its complexity — the number of inputs and outputs, the rules that relate them, and the number of exceptions. Some control functions, like automatic aircraft landing devices, are inherently complex and others can be made complex by providing alternative courses of action if any part of the system should fail.

The overall size of a hardware system is directly connected to the complexity of the control function. This fact forces a practical limit to complexity, since a system that is too large will be difficult to test and maintain, or even too bulky physically to fulfil its requirements. On the other hand the complexity of a microprocessor system can in principle be increased indefinitely, simply by adding more instructions to the program. There is practically no increase in size, or in the number of physical components.

Cost

Microprocessors now cost a negligible amount if bought in large quantities. They normally need to be equipped with power supplies and with other components such as stores; but even so, the component cost of a small microprocessor system is competitive with all but the very simplest electromechanical devices.

The design cost is a different matter. The most difficult part of designing a microprocessor system is the correct specification of the program. This needs relatively expensive equipment and some knowledge of computer science on the part of the design engineer. Furthermore, the need to learn a new technique has made the design costs of many microprocessor systems seem very high, but this can be regarded as an investment for the future. Nevertheless, it can still be argued that, to produce a simple control system in small quantities, a traditional hardwired approach is sometimes good economics.

Reliability

The reliability of a hardwired system depends on its size. Published statistics for the failure rates of individual components, soldered and wrapped joints can be used to calculate the 'Mean Time Between Faults' of any hardwired system. This figure can often be adjusted to any desired value by using more reliable components, improving ventilation, or duplicating or triplicating the whole system. This analysis assumes that the basic design is right; but since the behaviour of each separate control function can usually be checked independently, the assumption is usually valid.

Superficially, a system based on a microprocessor can be analysed in the same way. Since it has fewer components, it will appear far more reliable than its hardwired counterpart; but this again assumes that the design is correct. Here the assumption is dangerous, for most of the design in the system is in the controlling program, and it is far from easy to ensure that a series of instructions will always do exactly what they are intended to. There are two particular points to observe.

Firstly, mistakes in a program are errors in *design*. The failures they cause cannot be guarded against by duplication of the system (since both sets of equipment would make the same error at the same time), and they always come without prior warning.

Secondly, programming is an activity fraught with psychological difficulty. It has been compared to compulsive gambling. Most people are unreasoning optimists about their programs, and just as the gambler 'knows' that this time he has at last understood the mysterious forces behind the ivory ball, and that he must win on the next spin, so the programmer feels a moral certainty that his program is right. This conviction continues even though error after error comes to light; the programmer is always sure that every mistake is the last one. This universal tendency makes it very difficult to adopt the pessimistic, cynical viewpoint that alone can lead to programs that are genuinely correct. In practice, many control systems are fitted with programs that are only partially tested and riddled with mistakes. The accuracy of the program is the greatest single factor in determining the reliability of any microprocessor system. Methods of checking programs and verifying their correctness will be discussed at length later.

A classification of microprocessors

The market for microprocessors has expanded rapidly, and many different kinds are available.

Two important ways of making electronic circuitry are the 'bipolar' and 'MOS' technologies. Bipolar integrated circuits are about ten times faster than those made with MOS, but each transistor takes more room and dissipates more heat. This places a strict limit on the number of transistors on a chip, and therefore on the complexity of the chip as a whole. Most bipolar microprocessors take the form of 'bit slices' — components that can be put together in various ways to build powerful computers. The application areas and design methods for bit slices are somewhat specialised and entirely different from those associated with MOS microprocessors, and will not be considered further here.

With MOS technology, one chip can contain enough components to form a self-contained computer, albeit one that runs rather slower than a minicomputer or 'mainframe' machine. Most existing microprocessors are based on MOS.

Within this group, there is still a huge selection of devices. They share a common basic architecture, but differ in speed, in the amount of information they can handle at any time, in the complexity of the operations they actually do, in the way they are connected to the external world, in their power-supply requirements, and in their immunity to mechanical vibration and electrical noise. Other factors that might affect the selection of a microprocessor for a particular task are the number of manufacturers (to ensure continuity of supply) and the provision of software aids. Perhaps the most important single point is the degree to which the system design engineer is familiar with a particular type of microprocessor; the sheer labour of learning about a new family of microprocessors is so great that brand loyalty becomes a virtue.

Summary

This introductory chapter has made the following points:

- Microprocessors have a very low cost, and are extremely flexible in use. This combination offers many large application areas for exploitation.
- Microprocessors can be used to implement control functions of any complexity.
- The reliability of a microprocessor system depends chiefly on the accuracy of the controlling program. Correct programs are difficult and expensive to design.

2

Representation of data

This and the next few chapters deal with the intellectual and practical tools that the designer of a microprocessor system will need. The reader is advised to scan the material once for an overview – to look, as it were, into the tool cupboard – and then to return to it later, when he has begun work on an actual problem.

The binary system

Microprocessors are essentially devices for handling and processing *information*. In a digital system information is represented by binary digits, each of which can have only two possible values: 1 and 0. (These values often have other names, like 'true and false', 'set and clear', or 'mark and space'. The actual names used are not important, so long as it is understood that, for example, '1', 'true', 'set' and 'mark' all mean the same thing.)

In most circumstances, binary digits (or 'bits') are not handled singly, but in groups of fixed size called 'bytes' or 'words'. Various microprocessors have words of 4, 6, 8, 12 or 16 bits. However, eight bits is a useful and common word size, and we shall assume it in our examples.

The bits in a computer word have no predetermined meaning. Their significance always depends on the context, and is fully controlled by the system designer. There are, however, four basic types of information, each with its own conventions and methods of being handled: Boolean information, numerical information, character codes, and machine code.

Boolean information

Boolean information is the name used for data items that can have only two possible values, such as 'set' or 'clear'. On the input side, Boolean items may be derived from switch settings, relays or comparators. On output, Boolean signals control lamps, alarms, and other devices with simple 'on/off' characteristics.

Clearly, a Boolean data item can be mapped on to a single binary digit. One possible coding is for 'on' to be represented by 1 and 'off' by 0.

A word of eight binary digits can be used to contain up to eight different independent Boolean data items. If the items are related to one another (like the pushbuttons in a lift car) they are often packed into a single word; but otherwise it is more convenient to give each Boolean item a word to itself. By convention, the value is replicated, so that 'on' is represented by 11111111, and 'off' by 00000000.

Numerical information

Much of the data in any system is in the form of numbers. The values can be derived from external sources through A/D converters, or they can be generated internally whilst a program is being executed.

In a word with eight binary digits, there are 2^8 or 256 different combinations of 0's and 1's. *In principle*, these combinations can be used to represent numbers in any arbitrary code whatsoever. In practical terms, however, it is best to keep to some variant of the binary (radix two) notation, because microprocessors are designed to do arithmetic on this assumption.

The binary notation is a positional system, identical in principle to the denary system used in everyday life. A denary number is implicitly written with a radix of ten; it is understood that the various digits refer to units, tens, hundreds, thousands, etc., which are all powers of ten. Thus '1978' is interpreted as:

$$1 \times 10^3 + 9 \times 10^2 + 7 \times 10^1 + 8 \times 10^0$$

(The reader will remember that $10^0 = 1$.) An important point about the denary system is that it uses only ten different symbols: 0, 1, 2, 3, 4, 5, 6, 7, 8 and 9. Numbers greater than nine are written using combinations of the basic symbols.

In the binary system, the radix is two, and the only symbols needed are 0 and 1. A number like '10110' is interpreted as:

$$1 \times 2^4 + 0 \times 2^3 + 1 \times 2^2 \times 1 \times 2^1 + 0 \times 2^0$$

which equals 'twenty-two'.

Binary numbers are in general about three times longer (in terms of digits) than their decimal counterparts. The advantage of using binary numbers within a computer is that arithmetic is very simple.

Addition, for example, is governed by the table:

```
0 + 0 = 0
0 + 1 = 1
1 + 0 = 1
1 + 1 = 0, carry 1
```

The addition of two binary numbers could be written as follows:

$$
\begin{array}{r}
101101 \\
10111 \ + \\
\hline
1000100
\end{array}
\qquad
\left(
\begin{array}{r}
45 \\
23 \ + \\
\hline
68
\end{array}
\right)
$$

It is sometimes necessary to convert numbers between their denary and binary forms. Conversion from denary is best made by repeatedly dividing by two, and noting down the remainder each time. Finally the remainder digits are assembled, the first on the right and the last on the left. For example, to convert 87 to binary, we put:

①
$$\frac{43}{2)87} \quad \text{r } 1$$

②
$$\frac{21}{2)43} \quad \text{r } 1$$

③
$$\frac{10}{2)21} \quad \text{r } 1$$

④
$$\frac{5}{2)10} \quad \text{r } 0$$

⑤
$$\frac{2}{2)5} \quad \text{r } 1$$

⑥
$$\frac{1}{2)2} \quad \text{r } 0$$

⑦
$$\frac{0}{2)1} \quad \text{r } 1$$

⑦ . . . ①
$$\therefore 87 = 1010111$$

To make the conversion the other way, it is easiest to use a table of the powers of two:

$$
\begin{array}{ll}
2^0 = 1 & 2^5 = 32 \\
2^1 = 2 & 2^6 = 64 \\
2^2 = 4 & 2^7 = 128 \\
2^3 = 8 & 2^8 = 256 \\
2^4 = 16 & 2^9 = 512 \qquad \text{etc.}
\end{array}
$$

The conversion is made by adding up those powers of two represented by 1's in the binary number. For example:

$$
\begin{array}{rl}
1010111 = 2^6 + 2^4 + 2^2 + 2^1 + 2^0 = & 64 \\
& 16 \\
& 4 \\
& 2 \\
& \underline{1} \ + \\
= & 87
\end{array}
$$

These methods are suitable for humans, who normally think in the denary system. For a being (or a machine) that normally worked in the binary system the methods would be inverted, relying on division by ten, and a table of powers of ten.

The binary system is used in a number of variants, three of which will now be described.

Unsigned binary numbers

In this notation, numbers are represented in straightforward binary code. The only difference is that each number always has a fixed number of digits (eight in our examples). This implies that small numbers have leading zeros, and that there is a maximum size to the numbers that can be represented at all. For example:

00000011 = three

11111111 = two hundred and fifty-five (the largest number in an eight-bit system)

The presence of the leading zeros matters very little, but programmers must constantly be aware of the size limitation. Any calculation that could give a result greater than this limit may simply go wrong unless special precautions are used. Thus:

```
  11111010          (250)
  00001010    +      (10)
(1)00000100
```

The carry from the most significant stage of the addition drops off the end, leaving the (incorrect) answer 4.

Binary coded decimal ('BCD')

If a microprocessor is controlling a display made up of decimal digits, or reading decimal numbers from a keyboard, it is often convenient to allow each eight-bit word to represent one decimal digit. The binary code normally used for each digit is:

0 = 00000000   3 = 00000011

1 = 00000001   4 = 00000100

2 = 00000010   5 = 00000101

6 = 00000110   8 = 00001000

7 = 00000111   9 = 00001001

This system has two advantages: conversion to the true decimal form is trivial, and by using enough words (one for each digit) it is possible to represent numbers of any size. On the other hand, BCD is wasteful of space, and arithmetic is slow. The addition of two BCD digits is governed by the rule:

1. Add the two numbers as if they were (simple) binary quantities.
2. Add the carry from the previous stage (if any).
3. If the result is greater than ten, then:
    (a) subtract ten from the result,
    (b) carry 1 to the next stage.

For example:

$$
\begin{array}{c}
0011 \\
0101 \quad + \\
\hline
1000
\end{array}
\qquad
\left(
\begin{array}{c}
3 \\
5 \ + \\
\hline
8
\end{array}
\right)
$$

This is correct; but

$$
\begin{array}{c}
1000 \\
1001 \quad + \\
\hline
10001
\end{array}
\qquad
\left(
\begin{array}{c}
8 \\
9 \ + \\
\hline
17
\end{array}
\right)
$$

This exceeds ten, so 1010 (ten in binary) is subtracted:

$$
\begin{array}{c}
10001 \\
1010 \quad - \\
\hline
111
\end{array}
$$

giving 0111 (seven), and 1 is carried to the next stage.

In an eight-bit system, it is clearly possible to 'pack' two BCD digits into one word. For example, 10010111 in packed BCD means '97'.

Some combinations of bits would imply 'decimal digits' greater than nine, and are not permitted. Thus the eight-bit word '10101011' would be meaningless in packed BCD.

Signed binary numbers

In many applications it is important to be able to use *signed* numbers – numbers that can have negative or positive values. Humans normally use the sign-magnitude notation, where the absolute value of the number is preceded by its sign. This leads to complicated rules for the addition and subtraction of signed numbers, such as:

To add two signed numbers *a* and *b*:
- If the signs are the same, add the magnitudes and attach the common sign.
- If the signs are different, then:
  if the magnitude of *a* is greater than the magnitude of *b*, subtract *b* from *a* and attach the sign of *a*; *otherwise* subtract *a* from *b* and attach the sign of *b*.

The system used in microprocessors is quite different and much simpler. It is called the 'two's complement' notation.

In the discussion on unsigned binary numbers, it was noted that, where quantities grew too large, carries were lost and the results of addition were wrong. This was represented as a serious drawback; but in the two's complement notation the same feature is actually turned to advantage.

One way of defining a negative number $-n$ is to specify that it is the number that, when added to $+n$, will give zero. In a system with a limited number of digits, every number has its negative. For example:

```
00000001
11111111   +
```
$\overline{}$
(1)00000000

Here the carry is lost from the end, and the sum of the two numbers being added is zero. Since the first number is +1, the second is evidently −1. Similar arguments can be used to show that:

```
11111110 = −2
11111101 = −3
11111100 = −4   etc.
```

With this representation, the addition and subtraction of signed numbers is trivially easy: no account at all need be taken of the sign! For example, +7 + (−4) gives:

```
00000111
11111100   +
```
(1)00000011   = +3

The one drawback of this system is its potential ambiguity; does 11111010 mean '250' or '−6'? The answer to this question is fundamentally a matter of convention; but to arrive at a sensible rule we make use of a circle diagram.

Consider a variable with integral (whole number) values. Each value can be written down in a small circle, and the operation of adding 1 can be shown as an arrow. A mathematician would show part of the set of integers as in *Figure 2.1*, it being understood (by the mathematician) that the line of numbers extends to infinity in both directions.

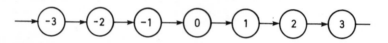

Figure 2.1

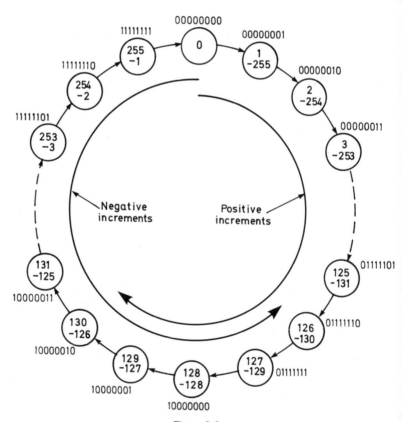

Figure 2.2

In a microprocessor with an eight-bit word, the line is not infinite at all; by starting at 0 and adding 1 repeatedly, one eventually arrives at 11111111 (255) and the next addition returns to zero because the carry from the left is lost.

A better representation of the diagram is therefore a circle, as in *Figure 2.2*. Starting from zero, the numbers 1, 2, 3 . . . are put in consecutive places, going clockwise right round to 255. This corresponds to our normal (unsigned) convention. Again starting from zero, the negative numbers are put in consecutive places going anti-clockwise. The binary representations of the numbers are written close by each circle. The diagram shows the ambiguity of the system; each binary group except zero can, in principle, stand for two different numbers, one of either sign.

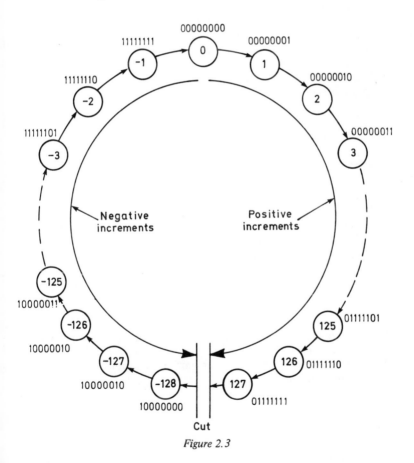

Figure 2.3

The diagram suggests a way of resolving this difficulty. If the circle is cut, somewhere opposite zero, then the assignment of numbers past this point in either direction can be stopped and the ambiguity removed. We obtain the result shown in *Figure 2.3*.

If this convention is observed, the values of the eight-bit number can range from −128, through 0, to +127. There are as many non-negative numbers as negative ones.

The exact place for the cut is chosen so that all negative numbers start with a '1'. This gives a very simple method of checking the sign of any number. The most significant digit is called the 'sign bit'.

As always, the system designer needs to exercise great care when using signed numbers. If the expected range is small, the system works automatically and the 'curvature' of the number scheme can be ignored, but with larger numbers special precautions must be taken.

This section has described four different systems of number representation, and it has been hinted that there are others as well. Let the reader be assured that these systems are tools, to be brought out, sharpened and used when they happen to be the right ones for a particular job, but otherwise kept in a dark and inconspicuous corner of the toolkit and ignored.

Character codes

Microprocessors are frequently used to communicate with people, through keyboards, visual display units and teletypes. The unit of communication in this context is the 'character'. Characters are represented by the universally accepted ASCII standard code (the initials stand for American Standard Code for Information Exchange). The code includes the following groups of symbols, most of which correspond to the keys on a typewriter:

- all capital letters;
- all lower-case letters;
- the ten decimal digits;
- various punctuation symbols;
- layout control symbols 'space', 'carriage return', 'line feed', 'tabulate' and 'form feed';
- various control symbols like 'end of transmission', 'ring bell' and 'acknowledge'.

A complete list of the ASCII code is given in Appendix 1. There are 128 defined symbols, so seven bits are enough to represent any one of them without ambiguity.

In most practical systems, the characters are transmitted and received as *eight*-bit codes. The extra bit is attached at left of the code. It is normally used as a 'parity' digit, and helps to detect errors in transmission. When a character is transmitted, the parity bit is chosen so as to make the total number of 1's in the character *even*. Thus:

ASCII for 'A' = 1000001;   'A' with parity = 01000001

ASCII for 'C' = 1000011;   'C' with parity = 11000011

When the character is received, the total number of 1's is counted. If it is odd, some of the digits in the number must have been corrupted and an error is known to have occurred. The system will not catch errors in which an even number of bits are affected; but in practice most errors are due to short voltage spikes, bits of fluff in paper tape, or other 'small' disturbances, and affect only one bit; so the system works well.

Inside a microprocessor, characters are handled as eight-bit quantities. The parity bit is usually stripped off, and replaced by zero, to make the numerical order of the codes the same as the alphabetical order of the letters. This is often useful.

Machine code

The last basic type of information inside a microprocessor is 'machine code'. This is a representation of the instructions that make up the program the machine is to execute. Its form depends on the exact brand of microprocessor used, and will be discussed extensively in later chapters.

3

Basic structure of a microprocessor

A diagram of a simple microprocessor system is shown in *Figure 3.1*. There are four essential components:

- a *store*, which retains information and produces it when needed;
- a *processing unit*, which moves and processes data, and which exercises control over the system;
- one or more *peripheral interface units*, which allow communication with the outside world;
- a *bus*, which forms a communication link between all the other parts.

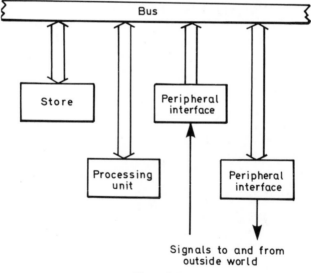

Figure 3.1

In very small systems all four components can be fabricated on to one chip, which then needs only a power supply to carry out its function. In most cases, however, each of the components is implemented in one or more separate integrated circuits.

The store

The store of the microprocessor is a rectangular array of binary digits, organised as shown in *Figure 3.2*. Each row of bits forms a word or cell, and is always handled as a single entity. The number of cells available varies widely between a few hundred and several thousand, but is always an exact power of two or a small multiple of such a number.

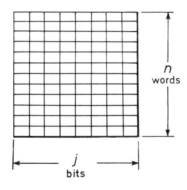

Figure 3.2

In computing jargon, the number 1024 (2^{10}) is called a 'K'. Thus a '4K eight-bit store' would have 4096 cells of eight bits each.

In any store, each cell has its own numerical address. The addresses often start from 0 and always increase in steps of 1. The last cell in a 4K store has address 4095.

Stores can be bought in two basic varieties: RAM and ROM. The letters RAM stand for *random-access memory*. Such a memory can record any information presented to it, and reproduce it later. The memory has two modes of operation, 'write' and 'read'.

To *write* information, the store is supplied with an address (expressed as a binary number), a data word, and a suitable control signal. The data word is recorded in the cell selected by the address, replacing any information that may have been there previously. No other cell in the store is affected.

To *read* information back, the store is again supplied with an address. It responds by producing the contents of the selected cell on its output lines. The operation is non-destructive; it does not alter any of the information in the store.

The time needed to read or write information is known as the 'cycle time' of the store. In most present-day systems it is a fraction of a microsecond. The phrase 'random access' is used because any cell in the store can be reached equally quickly. The data is not ordered as it would be on a magnetic tape.

ROM stands for *read-only memory*. As its name implies, the data in a block of ROM can be read, but it cannot be altered, at least in normal running. ROMs are used for information that is fixed for the lifetime of the system, such as the instructions of the controlling program or sets of numerical constants. The information is implanted either during manufacture or by a special process called 'field programming', which is normally non-reversible. (Special EPROMs — erasable programmable read-only memory — have the property that information can be deleted by a long exposure to ultraviolet light. EPROMs have various disadvantages, including long access times and a high price.)

Since a ROM cannot be written to, the 'cycle time' is meaningless; instead, one uses the term 'access time', which is the time needed to fetch the contents of any cell. Again, this is of the order of a microsecond or less.

The names ROM and RAM are misleading, because access to any selected cell is equally fast in either type; logically, ROM is a type of RAM. However, the convention that RAM means specifically 'writeable random-access memory.' is widely accepted, and will be used in this book.

In general, ROM is rather cheaper than RAM. A more important difference is that RAM is volatile. If there is a loss of power the information in a RAM disappears, whereas in a ROM it is retained. These two considerations suggest that any system should use ROM, rather than RAM, wherever possible.

The central processing unit

The central processing unit (CPU) has the job of fetching instructions from the store and executing them, one by one. We shall begin by describing the very simple, hypothetical CPU that is shown diagrammatically in *Figure 3.3*.

In the model, the CPU contains three registers, and some combinatorial arithmetic and control circuitry. It is driven by a series of clock pulses, each of which produces some change in the states of the

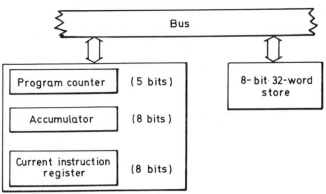

Figure 3.3

registers. The precise action of the electronics will not be discussed, but attention will be centred on the registers and on the way their contents are changed.

The store associated with this CPU has only 32 words. Any cell can therefore be selected by a five-bit address.

A cycle begins when the CPU is ready to fetch the next instruction from the store and begin its execution. At this point, the *program counter register* contains the five-bit address of the cell from which the next instruction is to be fetched and obeyed. The first pulse causes this address to be sent to the store, where it selects the contents of one of the cells. These contents are sent back along the bus and placed in the *current instruction register.*

The instruction that has just been fetched is a collection of binary digits, and to be executed correctly it must first be decoded. The instruction format, which is a basic property of the CPU design, is this:

F	F	F	A	A	A	A	A
function			address				

The *function* specifies what is to be done, and the *address* usually indicates which cell in the memory is to be used in doing it.

Three bits give us eight different functions. For our hypothetical example we shall divide them into groups, and give each one a code or *mnemonic* to make it easier to remember.

Group 1 is concerned with arithmetic. The third register in the CPU is called the *accumulator,* and is used to hold the partial results of calculations, in much the same way as the display register of a calculator.

Group 1 has four instructions:

LOAD (F = 000) Copy the contents of the selected cell into the accumulator.

STORE (F = 001) Copy the contents of the accumulator back to the selected cell.

ADD (F = 010) Fetch the contents of the selected cell and *add* it to the accumulator.

SUB (F = 011) Fetch the contents of the selected cell and *subtract* it from the accumulator.

During the second pulse, the CPU decodes and executes the current instruction. In the case of a Group 1 instruction, it also adds 1 to the program counter, so that the following instruction, to be executed on the next cycle, is taken from the store cell adjacent to the current one.

Programs consist of sequences of instructions. The following fragment will add the numbers in cells 20 and 21, subtract the number in cell 22, and place the result in cell 23.

LOAD	20	00010100
ADD	21	01010101
SUB	22	01110110
STORE	23	00110111

(mnemonic version)   (binary version)

The mnemonic version uses denary addresses and is convenient to write and read, whereas the binary version is the one that is actually executed. The relationship between the two should be noted carefully. Thus, the function code for SUB is 011, and the binary equivalent of 22 is 10110; so 'SUB 22' becomes 01110110.

Another point worth emphasising is that the addresses in the instructions are indeed *addresses* and not *operands*; each indicates the place from which the corresponding operand is to be fetched. Thus the result of the program depends on the contents of *cells* 20, 21 and 22; it is nothing to do with the *numbers* 20, 21 and 22.

The second group of instructions is concerned with transfer of control. The instructions in the first group, as the reader will remember, are invariably fetched from consecutive cells in the store. If they were the only instructions available, every program would be limited to sequences of 32 instructions at most, and the system would be unable to repeat any sequence or decide on alternative courses of action.

Group 2 has two instructions:

JUMP (F = 100) Take the next instruction from the given address, instead of the one next in sequence.

JSBC (F = 101) Test the most significant bit in the accumulator; if it is zero take the next instruction from the given address. Otherwise take the next one in sequence. (The mnemonic stands for 'Jump if Sign Bit Clear'.)

The fragment of program on page 22 would have worked equally well from any four consecutive cells in the store (except, of course 20-23). To use Group 2 instructions, however, a specific set of cells must be chosen so that the destinations of the jumps can be filled in. We shall follow the convention of starting programs in address zero.

Here are two simple examples. The first fragment of program places into cell 29 the modulus or absolute value of the number in cell 31. It is assumed that the number is in two's complement notation, and that cell 30 holds zero.

Address	*Instruction*		
(0)	LOAD	31	Copy contents of cell 31 to accumulator.
(1)	JSBC	4	Jump to cell 4 if accumulator positive (i.e. if sign bit = 0).
(2)	LOAD	30	Clear accumulator to 0.
(3)	SUB	31	Subtract contents of cell 31.
(4)	STORE	29	Store result in cell 29.
(29)	0		(Place for result)
(30)	0		
(31)	n		(Number to be used)

The second example multiplies the two numbers m and n in cells 30 and 31, leaving the answer in cell 29. It is assumed that m and n are not negative (they may be zero), and that cells 27 and 28 contain 0 and 1 respectively. The method works by decrementing n by 1 and repeatedly adding m to a partial product. The process stops when n becomes negative. (This method of multiplication is not recommended for general use: it is far too slow. Here it has the merit of simplicity.)

(0)	LOAD	27	
(1)	STORE	29	Set partial product to zero.
(2)	LOAD	31	
(3)	SUB	28	Take 1 from *n*.
(4)	STORE	31	
(5)	JSBC	7	Skip to 7 if result still not negative.
(6)	JUMP	11	Jump to end of program.
(7)	LOAD	29	
(8)	ADD	30	Add *m* to partial product.
(9)	STORE	29	
(10)	JUMP	2	Go back and repeat loop.
(11)	JUMP	11	Next part of program. Stop by executing this instruction repeatedly.

If the reader has any difficulty in following the program, it often helps to write out a *trace*, in which the history of every variable quantity is reproduced in detail. The trace for the program is shown in *Figure 3.4*, for the calculation of 4 × 3. This trace shows that the result, 12, is indeed generated in location 29. The program has some generality about it; it could be expected to work with other pairs of numbers, provided that the product did not exceed the allowable range of numbers 0 to 127.

It is worth noting that the written length of the program, or lexicographic length, is 11 instructions, but the dynamic length, or number of instructions actually executed, is 32 for the sample of data chosen. This difference in lengths is a general feature of programs that involve repetition of any kind.

The last group of instructions is concerned with input and output, and will be discussed in the next section.

Peripheral interface units

Within a microprocessor, data is handled in words of a fixed number of bits (eight in our example). Physically, the signals representing these bits must be suitable for direct connection to a MOS LSI chip.

Information derived from the outside world is hardly ever in this convenient form. Many signals are essentially analogue in nature; others may be digital but incompatible with MOS levels, and some may be liable to occasional voltage spikes that would destroy any MOS circuit to which they were directly connected. The same is true on the output side; in a control system the microprocessor will in general activate motors, lamps and relays that need high currents to operate.

Program counter	Instruction register	Accumulator	Cells 29	30	31
			?	4	3
0	LOAD 27	0			
1	STORE 29	0	0		
2	LOAD 31	3			
3	SUB 28	2			
4	STORE 31	2			2
5	JSBC 7	2			
7	LOAD 29	0			
8	ADD 30	4			
9	STORE 29	4	4		
10	JUMP 2				
2	LOAD 31	2			
3	SUB 28	1			
4	STORE 31	1			1
5	JSBC 7	1			
7	LOAD 29	4			
8	ADD 30	8			
9	STORE 29	8	8		
10	JUMP 2				
2	LOAD 31	1			
3	SUB 28	0			
4	STORE 31	0			0
5	JSBC 7	0			
7	LOAD 29	8			
8	ADD 30	12			
9	STORE 29	12	12		
10	JUMP 2				
2	LOAD 31	0			
3	SUB 28	−1			
4	STORE 31				−1
5	JSBC 7				
6	JUMP 11				
11	JUMP 11	−1	12	4	−1

etc.

Figure 3.4

External devices are usually connected to the microprocessor through a two-stage system, as shown in *Figure 3.5*. When arriving from an external source, every signal is first fed to a 'signal conditioner'. This unit has the job of reducing the signal to a binary word at the appropriate signal levels for the microprocessor system. The construction of the signal conditioner will depend on the circumstances; it will often consist of an A/D converter, or an optical isolator, or a level changer.

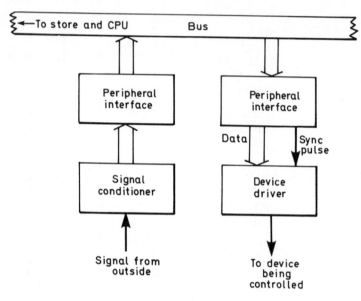

Figure 3.5

The peripheral interface is used to connect the conditioned signal to the bus. It ensures that the signal is made available in an orderly manner. Each peripheral interface has its own address, and acts very like a store cell, in that it admits the signal to the bus only when it sees its own address and the appropriate control signal on the bus.

The output side works in a similar way. The peripheral interface contains a one-word register, and any information to be sent to the environment outside is strobed into this register by the appropriate address and control signals on the bus. Once in the register, the data is connected to the device driver, which may typically contain D/A converters or power transistors to activate the machinery being controlled. A synchronising pulse may also be produced every time that the contents of the peripheral interface are changed.

In general, the peripheral interfaces are regarded as being part of the microprocessor system, whereas the signal conditioners and device drivers are not. The interface, or boundary, comes between the two.

There is no practical limit to the number of peripheral interfaces or the number of signals that can be connected to a microprocessor system. In the diagram, each interface deals with only one signal, but there is no reason why one interface should not handle several signals, provided that the information they represent can be packed into a single word. Signals from a set of eight lift buttons or a coded keyboard would normally be handled by a single interface.

On the other hand, some signals might need two or even more interfaces. Examples are the outputs of high-precision A/D converters, links from computers with long words, or connections to registers with many stages.

It is now possible to define the 'Group 3' instructions for our hypothetical machine. In these instructions, the address parts do not specify cells in the store, but individual peripheral interfaces.

INPUT $(F = 110)$ Read a word from the stated peripheral interface and put it into the accumulator.

OUTPUT $(F = 111)$ Send the contents of the accumulator to the stated peripheral interface.

These instructions can be illustrated by some simple examples. Consider a traffic light controller for a four-way intersection. The lights are controlled by a bank of eight relays, grouped as follows:

Signs for pedestrians		*East-west route*			*North-south route*		
Red man	Green man	Red	Amber	Green	Red	Amber	Green

Suppose that the relays are connected to peripheral interface 0. Then the following sequence will illuminate red and amber on the east-west route, and red on the north-south route:

LOAD   31   Cell 31 contains the constant 52, which, in *binary*,
OUTPUT   0   is 00110100. The 1's in this constant correspond to
. . .   the lights to be switched on.

(31) 52

Traffic lights need to be properly timed. One possible form of timer is an eight-bit register that is decremented once a second, that can be preset by the microcomputer system to any initial value, and that can be read back at any time. A suitable configuration is shown in *Figure 3.6.*

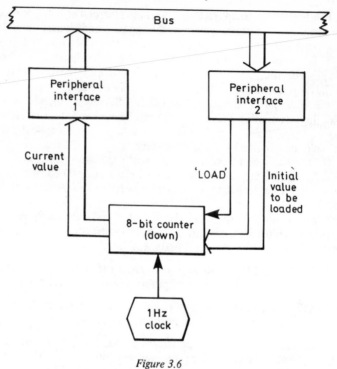

Figure 3.6

A delay of any number of seconds up to 128 (say n) can be engineered by presetting the counter to $(n - 1)$, and then waiting for its contents to become negative. A sequence of code for waiting 10 seconds would be:

(0)	LOAD	30	Cell 30 contains the constant 9.
(1)	OUTPUT	2	
(2)	┌►INPUT	1	Read contents of counter.
(3)	└─JSBC	1	Jump back if not negative.
(4)	. . .		Proceed with the next part of the program.

The bus

The details of the bus follow inevitably from the properties of the other components in the microprocessor system.

The bus is controlled by the CPU, which forms the origin of most of the signals. The following groups must be present:

- *Address lines.* Enough are needed to be able to select every cell in the store.
- *Data lines.* These are used to transmit words of information between the CPU and the other units. There must be one data line for each bit in the word. Data lines must be bi-directional.
- *Control lines.* Control is needed to indicate whether an address refers to the memory or to a peripheral interface, and whether the operation is to read (data flow towards the CPU) or to write (data flow away from CPU).
- *Clock.* The CPU clock must be transmitted to all other components to help with synchronisation.

Our hypothetical computer would have five address lines, eight data lines, two control lines and one clock line, making 16 in all. In practice this is a very low number, and 50-100 is more typical of real systems.

4

Assembly language

Chapter 3 described a simple hypothetical computer, and presented some programs for this machine. For the most part, these programs were not written in binary, but in an informal notation that included addresses, mnemonics (such as LOAD and INPUT) and constants (such as '52'). This chapter will give a formal description of the notation, which is often called 'assembly language'.

Assembly languages exist in considerable numbers, and in general they differ only in insignificant detail. The specific style of assembly language discussed here is a representative sample, but the reader is warned to observe any minor differences that may exist when transferring say, to an assembly language offered by a manufacturer.

A program as an engineering drawing

A near equivalent to a program is an engineering drawing. In many areas, such as electronics, drawings bear no physical resemblance to the machines they represent. They are easy to understand because they use standard symbols and conventions. This is also true of programs. A 'direct' representation of a program would be a table of 1's and 0's, and would be almost incomprehensible in that form. It is much better to use standard symbols, provided that one fully understands the meaning of the symbols in terms of the binary patterns they represent.

Another way of regarding a program is as a map. Just as an Ordnance Survey map describes the surface of each square kilometre of land, so a program describes the contents of each of the cells in the store. Most maps contain marginal information, such as keys for the symbols, the latitude and longitude of the lower left-hand corner of the map, the scale, and so on. Programs also contain marginal information.

Before a program can actually be used, it must be translated into its binary form and loaded into the store of the microprocessor system.

This translation can be done automatically by a computer program called an 'assembler'.

The elements of assembly language

Basically, an assembly language program is made up from a sequence of characters. The lexicon used includes all the letters, all the decimal digits, the space, and various punctuation symbols like + − * / ? # ( ) : , ; < > ↑ | and . The program is written on a number of lines. A good programmer will often add commentary to explain what the program is doing, but the extra text is not part of the program itself; so to keep it distinct, commentary is placed to the right of the symbol ↑, thus:

THIS IS	↑	THIS IS ALL
ALL PART	↑	COMMENTARY FOR THE
OF A	↑	HUMAN READER, AND FORMS NO
PROGRAM	↑	PART OF THE PROGRAM

As in natural language, the characters are made up into 'words'. There are four basic types of word: constants, symbols of constant meaning, names, and strings.

Constants

A constant stands for some known numerical value or pattern of bits. In Chapter 3, all constants were written using the decimal notation, including those that were meant to represent binary patterns without any numerical significance. For example, the binary pattern 00110100, which was supposed to mean 'red-and-amber east-west, red north-south', was written as '52'.

Assembly language offers three ways of writing a constant:

- as a decimal number;
- as a 'hexadecimal' number ('hex' for short):
- as an 'octal' number.

Hex constants are written in the base 16. Sixteen different symbols are required, and they are:

0   1   2   3   4   5   6   7   8   9   A   B   C   D   E   F

The advantage of using hex numbers is that they have a simple relationship to their binary equivalent. Since $16 = 2^4$, each hex digit corresponds to a group of four binary digits, according to the code:

binary	0000	0001	0010	0011	0100	0101	0110	0111
hex	0	1	2	3	4	5	6	7
binary	1000	1001	1010	1011	1100	1101	1110	1111
hex	8	9	A	B	C	D	E	F

This allows eight-bit binary numbers to be written as a pair of hex digits. For example:

00110100 = 34, 0011110 = 1E, 11111100 = FC

Some special notation is needed to distinguish hex numbers from decimal numbers or other words with similar appearance. There are two methods:

- The number is preceded by the sign '?'.
- The number is followed by an H. In this case the rule is that the *first* digit of the number must be in the range 0–9. This forces the programmer to precede the number with a zero if it would otherwise have started with one of the digits A to F.

Examples of hex notation are:

?34, 34H, ?1E, 1EH, ?FC, 0FCH

The *octal* notation is closely similar to hex, except that the binary digits are now grouped in threes. The eight symbols are:

0   1   2   3   4   5   6   7

Octal numbers may be written preceded by a $ sign or followed by the letter O. Some examples (having the same values as the examples of hex above) are:

$64, 64O, $36, 36O, $374, 374O

Symbols of constant meaning

Every assembly language has a set of symbols with fixed, predefined meanings. Some of them are single characters, like . or =, whilst others are constructed from groups of letters. The symbols fall into the following groups:

- punctuation symbols: , : . = etc.
- mnemonic codes for the various instructions, like LOAD, STORE, JSBC or OUTPUT.
- words that indicate 'marginal information', like TITLE or START.

The symbols with constant meaning are *reserved*, and may not be used for other purposes.

Names

In programming it is extremely convenient to refer to quantities without knowing their exact value. When a mathematician plans a calculation, he will do so in terms of symbolic quantities like x or y. The symbols are replaced by actual numbers at the latest possible moment, just before the calculation is actually made; this adds to the generality and flexibility of the planning process. In the same way, the constants and addresses in a program are often referred to by names, which are only replaced by their actual values when the program is translated into its binary form.

Every name in an assembly language consists of a letter, followed by further letters and/or decimal digits. Names can be chosen quite freely, except that they must never clash with mnemonics and other symbols of constant meaning. Examples of names are

TEMPERATURE   K1   FC   Q

The reader can now see the reason for insisting that hexadecimal numbers start with digits in the range 0 to 9. If they did not, there would be nothing to distinguish them from names.

Strings

For certain purposes, it is convenient to specify whole sequences of characters. Such a sequence is called a *string*, and it is written as a collection of characters enclosed in double quotes, thus:

"THIS IS A STRING"

Inside a string, characters are devoid of any intrinsic meaning, and are not split up into symbols, names, or numbers. The string as a whole is stored and later reproduced as a message to some human user.

Items

In an assembly language, the unit that specifies the contents of a memory cell is called an *item*.

The most common item is a machine instruction. This consists of a mnemonic, and an address, which may be given as a number or a symbolic name. The two parts are separated by one or more spaces, thus:

```
LOAD   30
JSBC   X5        ↑ X5 IS A SYMBOLIC NAME
```

Some items consist of numerical constants. The value of such an item is simply written down by itself:

```
J17Q             ↑ A SYMBOLIC CONSTANT
?FF              ↑ A HEX CONSTANT
39               ↑ A DECIMAL CONSTANT
```

Directives

A 'directive' is a piece of marginal information. Every program starts with a TITLE directive, written as follows:

> TITLE "A STRING"

where the string consists of a suitable title. Examples are:

> TITLE "TRAFFIC LIGHT CONTROLLER"

or

> TITLE "ROBOT SPEECH GENERATOR"

The title serves to identify the program, and to label any documentation that the assembler may generate.

To match the title, every program ends with a START directive. This is written on a line by itself, and consists of the reserved word START, followed by the address of the first instruction of the program to be executed (which is often, but not necessarily, the first to be written). The address may be in explicit or symbolic form, e.g.

```
      START 5
or    START J27
```

When items are translated, they are placed in adjacent cells of the store. It is normally necessary to specify the address of the first cell, and this is done by another directive:

> . = address

With this directive the address is usually in numerical form. For example:

```
  = 5
  ITEM A
  ITEM B
  ITEM C
```

implies that ITEM A is to go into cell 5, ITEM B into cell 6, and ITEM C into cell 7. The address can be reset part-way through a program if necessary.

We have covered enough material to be able to present a program in formal assembly language. Here, then, is the multiplication program given in Chapter 3:

```
TITLE "MULTIPLICATION BY REPEATED ADDITION"
. = 0        ↑ FOLLOWING ITEMS INTENDED FOR CELLS 0
             ↑ ONWARDS
LOAD 27      ↑ SET PARTIAL PRODUCT TO ZERO
STORE 29
LOAD 31      ↑ TAKE 1 FROM N
SUB 28
STORE 31
JSBC 7       ↑ JUMP IF RESULT NOT NEGATIVE
JUMP 11      ↑ JUMP TO END OF PROGRAM
LOAD 29      ↑ ADD M TO PARTIAL PRODUCT
ADD 30
STORE 29
JUMP 2       ↑ GO BACK AND REPEAT LOOP
JUMP 11      ↑ STOP
. = 27       ↑ FOLLOWING ITEMS MEANT FOR CELLS 27
             ↑ ONWARDS
0
1
0            ↑ PLACE FOR PRODUCT
4            ↑ MULTIPLIER
3            ↑ MULTIPLICAND
START 0
```

The use of names

The program just given is full of addresses that have had to be found by counting (such as 2, 7 or 11) or by arbitrary assignment (such as 27 or 31). Both methods are tedious and liable to error. This fact is barely evident in this short program, but presents insuperable difficulty in programs of any realistic size (hundreds or thousands of instructions). The drawbacks are particularly severe when a program has to be changed. For example, if an extra instruction had to be inserted between those in cells 2 and 3 to correct an error, all the instructions below would be shuffled down by one cell and '7' and '11' would have to be changed to '8' and '12'. This requirement, to alter sections of the program that are already correct and remote from any actual error, is so tedious to carry out that it can introduce further errors, leading to a never-ending cycle of corrections, trials, and further corrections.

All these difficulties can be overcome by using names. Any item can be labelled with a name, as follows:

NAME: ITEM

(Note the position of the colon immediately following the name.) Once an item is named, it can be referred to by its name instead of its position in the store. The assembler will replace the name by the address automatically, so that for the program writer the name is independent of its position. No changes need be made if items are moved around in the store.

Names can be attached both to instructions and to constants, and they can be used to refer to items that occur anywhere in the program. We say that 'forward' as well as 'backward' references are permitted.

Using names, the program becomes:

```
TITLE "MULTIPLICATION BY REPEATED ADDITION"
. = 0
KATE:   LOAD ZERO      ↑ NOTE THAT ZERO,
        STORE PP       ↑ ONE, PP, M AND N
JOHN:   LOAD N         ↑ ARE ALL THE NAMES OF
        SUB ONE        ↑ CELLS HOLDING NUMBERS
        STORE N        ↑ KATE, JOHN, ANN AND
        JSBC ANN       ↑ JOE ARE THE NAMES OF
        JUMP JOE       ↑ SPECIFIC INSTRUCTIONS
ANN:    LOAD PP
        ADD M
        STORE PP
        JUMP JOHN
JOE:    JUMP JOE       ↑ STOP HERE
. = 27
ZERO:   0
ONE:    1
PP:     0
M:      3
N:      4
START   KATE
```

Definitions

Sometimes it is useful to give a name some constant value rather than attaching it to an item as a label. This can be done by writing a *definition*, as follows:

NAME: = VALUE

where the name is again arbitrary, and the value is a number. If a name has been defined in this way, it can be used instead of the value throughout the program.

· The chief value of this facility lies in writing programs that it is thought may need to be changed later. For example, consider a program that refers extensively to peripheral interface 3. Two possible versions are:

(a)   (b)

                          P:= 3
OUTPUT 3   OUTPUT P
. . .   . . .
. . .   . . .
OUTPUT 3   OUTPUT P
. . .   . . .
. . .   . . .
OUTPUT 3   OUTPUT P
. . .   . . .
OUTPUT 3   OUTPUT P

Suppose that, for some reason, it became necessary to use a different peripheral interface, such as 8. In program (a), it would be necessary to change every output instruction. In program (b), however, only the definition need be altered.

A complete example

In Chapter 3 a method of controlling traffic lights was discussed, and some fragments of program were quoted. A complete program for this purpose will now be given. The traffic lights in question are to run on a fixed cycle, with the following timing:

Green N–S, red E–W	30 s
Amber N–S, red-and-amber E–W	5 s
Red N–S, green E–W	15 s
Red-and-amber N–S, amber E–W	5 s

The reader should consult pages 27 and 28, and then study the following program:

```
TITLE "CONTROLLER FOR TRAFFIC LIGHTS"
LIGHT:= 0                    ↑ INTERFACE FOR LIGHTS
ALARM:= 1                    ↑ INTERFACE TO READ IN STATE
                             ↑ OF CLOCK
CLOCK:= 2                    ↑ INTERFACE TO START CLOCK
. = 0
LOOP:   LOAD GNS             ↑ DISPLAY GREEN N-S
        OUTPUT LIGHT
        LOAD T30             ↑ START CLOCK (30 SECONDS)
        OUTPUT CLOCK
XA:     INPUT ALARM          ↑ WAIT UNTIL CLOCK < 0
        JSBC XA
        LOAD ANS             ↑ DISPLAY AMBER N-S
        OUTPUT LIGHT
        LOAD T5              ↑ START  CLOCK (5 SECONDS)
        OUTPUT CLOCK
XB:     INPUT ALARM          ↑ WAIT UNTIL CLOCK < 0
        JSBC XB
        LOAD RNS             ↑ DISPLAY RED N-S
        OUTPUT LIGHT
        LOAD T15             ↑ START CLOCK (15 SECONDS)
        OUTPUT CLOCK
XC:     INPUT ALARM          ↑ WAIT UNTIL CLOCK < 0
        JSBC XC
        LOAD RANS            ↑ DISPLAY RED AND AMBER N-S
        OUTPUT LIGHT
        LOAD T5              ↑ START CLOCK (5 SECONDS)
        OUTPUT  CLOCK
XD:     INPUT ALARM          ↑ WAIT UNTIL CLOCK < 0
        JSBC XD
        JUMP LOOP
↑ LIGHT CONTROLS FOLLOW AS OCTAL CONSTANTS
GNS:    $41                  ↑ GREEN NS, RED EW
ANS:    $62                  ↑ AMBER NS, RED AND AMBER EW
RNS:    $14                  ↑ RED NS, GREEN EW
RANS:   $26                  ↑ RED AND AMBER NS, AMBER EW
↑ NOW TIMING CONSTANTS (EACH ONE LESS THAN NUMBER
↑ OF SECONDS NEEDED)
T30:    29
T5:     4
T15:    14
START LOOP
```

```
SYMBOL              HEX    DEC    OCT
LIGHT                0      0      0
ALARM                1      1      1
CLOCK                2      2      2
LOOP                 0      0      0
GNS                 19     25     31
T30                 1D     29     35
XA                   4      4      4
ANS                 1A     26     32
T5                  1E     30     36
XB                   A     10     12
RNS                 1B     27     33
T15                 1F     31     37
XC                  10     16     20
RANS                1C     28     34
XD                  16     22     26


                1
                2  TITLE "CONTROLLER FOR TRAFFIC LIGHTS"
                3
                4  LIGHT:= 0          *INTERFACE FOR LIGHTS
                5  ALARM:=1           *INTERFACE FOR STATE OF CLOCK
                6  CLOCK:=2           *INTERFACE TO START CLOCK
                7
                8  .=0                *CODE TO START AT ADDRESS 0
                9
  0 19         10  LOOP:LOAD GNS    *DISPLAY GREEN N-S
  1 E0         11       OUTPUT LIGHT
  2 1D         12       LOAD T30       *START CLOCK (30 SECONDS)
  3 E2         13       OUTPUT CLOCK
  4 C1         14  XA:  INPUT ALARM    *WAIT UNTIL CLOCK < 0
  5 A4         15       JSBC XA
                16
  6 1A         17       LOAD ANS     *DISPLAY AMBER N-S
  7 E0         18       OUTPUT LIGHT
  8 1E         19       LOAD T5        *START CLOCK (5 SECONDS)
  9 E2         20       OUTPUT CLOCK
  A C1         21  XB:  INPUT ALARM    *WAIT TILL CLOCK <0
  B AA         22       JSBC XB
                23
  C 1B         24       LOAD RNS     *DISPLAY RED N-S
  D E0         25       OUTPUT LIGHT
  E 1F         26       LOAD T15       *START CLOCK (15 SECONDS)
  F E2         27       OUTPUT CLOCK
 10 C1         28  XC:  INPUT ALARM    *WAIT TILL CLOCK < 0
 11 B0         29       JSBC XC
                30
 12 1C         31       LOAD RANS    *DISPLAY RED AND AMBER N-S
 13 E0         32       OUTPUT LIGHT
 14 1E         33       LOAD T5        *START CLOCK (5 SECONDS)
 15 E2         34       OUTPUT CLOCK
 16 C1         35  XD:  INPUT ALARM    *WAIT UNTIL CLOCK < 0
 17 B6         36       JSBC XD
 18 80         37       JUMP LOOP
                38
                39  *     LIGHT CONTROLS FOLLOW AS OCTAL CONSTANTS
                40
 19 21         41  GNS: $41          *GREEN N-S, RED E-W
 1A 32         42  ANS: $62          *AMBER N-S, RED AND AMBER E-W
 1B  C         43  RNS: $14          *RED N-S, GREEN E-W
 1C 16         44  RANS: $26         *RED AND AMBER N-S, AMBER E-W
                45
                46  *     NOW TIMING CONSTANTS (EACH ONE LESS THAN
                47  *         THE NUMBER OF SECONDS NEEDED)
                48
 1D 1D         49  T30: 29
 1E  4         50  T5:  4
 1F  F         51  T15: 14
                52  START LOOP
  0 FAULTS AND    0 WARNINGS
```

Figure 4.1

Practical points

Once written, a program can be punched on to paper tape or cards, or keyed directly into a filing system on a computer. Then it will be run through the *assembler*, which translates it into binary, and produces a listing in the general style of *Figure 4.1*. This should be studied closely, for it gives not only a transcription of the program itself, but various details of its translation including the values of all the names and the precise translation into binary (shown as hex numbers at the left).

5

Some aspects of microprocessor design

The machine described in Chapter 3 was designed to give the reader an introduction to microprocessor concepts such as stores, programs, peripheral control and assembly languages. It was, however, far too small and primitive for general use — the reader will have noted that its store was strained to the utmost even to provide control for fixed-cycle traffic lights.

The chapter discusses some of the features that give microprocessors their flexibility, generality and power. Little will be said about the electronics of the devices, because it can be taken for granted that microprocessor chips should be small, fast, use as few pins as possible, run on standard supply voltages but consume almost no power, and interface cleanly with external logical circuitry. The points to be considered deal with various aspects of programming.

In broad terms, the features fall into three categories. The first consists of properties that are essential, and that must be included in the design of every microprocessor. The second group contains features that are highly desirable in that they aid programming, but that can nevertheless be discarded if necessary. The third group includes a selection of various optional features that may be useful in particular circumstances, but that would be redundant in the majority of practical applications. The entire discussion serves as a background against which the details of particular microprocessors can be measured; without this information, much of the design of a microprocessor would seem incomprehensible.

Essential features

Large address space

The address space of a microprocessor is the range or number of different store addresses it can use. This range is related to the number of binary digits in the address part of the instruction; for example, the hypothetical machine with five address bits could refer only to 2^5 or 32 different cells.

In practice, the range of addresses needed for application is usually much larger than 32, and cannot be determined exactly until the system is designed and tested. Every 'general-purpose' microprocessor must therefore have a large enough address space for any likely application. Most successful designs use 16 bits, which implies an address space of 2^{16} or 65 536 cells.

Logic operations

Many of the signals connected to microprocessors are Boolean, indicating the state of a switch or of an on/off indicator. Boolean variables can also be generated inside the system by comparisons or tests on numerical data. The microprocessor must be able to store and process these Boolean variables with the same flexibility as conventional hardwired logic. The store is already provided, so in principle all that is required is one universal logic operation such as NOR or NAND. In practice, most microprocessor designs recognise that it is often awkward to do all logical processing with only one function, and provide AND, OR and NOT instructions instead. These 'logic' instructions usually work on the contents of the accumulator and affect all the bits in parallel.

The AND operator will typically fetch one of its operands from the store, just like an ADD instruction. From then on, it considers its operands to be groups of bits without any numerical significance, and *and*'s each corresponding pair, leaving the result in the accumulator, thus:

Original contents of accumulator	01110011
Operand from store	01011010 *and*
Result	01010010

The OR instruction works in a similar way; its result is an *inclusive or*:

Original contents of accumulator	01110011
Operand from store	01011010 *or*
Result in accumulator	01111011

NOT is an instruction that uses only the contents of the accumulator. It simply reverses each digit.

Original contents of accumulator	01110011
After NOT operation	10001100

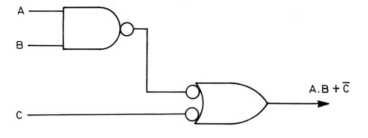

Figure 5.1

Logic operations form an alternative to hardware in evaluating Boolean expressions. Thus the expression $A.B + \overline{C}$ can be implemented either by a logic network (*Figure 5.1*) or by a sequence of instructions (which assumes that the cells with names A, B, C contain the corresponding Boolean values):

LOAD	A	↑ CALCULATE
AND	B	↑ A AND B
STORE	TEMP	↑ AND STORE
LOAD	C	↑ CALCULATE NOT C
NOT		↑ (NO ADDRESS REQUIRED)
OR	TEMP	↑ ACCUMULATOR CONTAINS $A.B + \overline{C}$

Shifts

A shift operation consists of moving a word (usually the contents of the accumulator) bodily one place left or right. If a word represents a number, a shift towards the left will effectively multiply the number by two, and a shift to the right will halve it. If the bits in a word represent several independent Boolean variables, a shift can be used to bring an individual digit to the sign bit position where it can be tested by an instruction like 'JSBC'.

Shift instructions in either direction have several variants, which differ in the rules applied at the ends of the word being shifted. In a *circular* shift, the bit that emerges from one end of the accumulator is fed round to the other end; in a *logical* shift, the bit that emerges is thrown away and a zero is fed in at the other end; and in an *arithmetic* shift (which is always to the right) the sign bit is replicated so that the result is correct for numbers of either sign (except for loss of fractions). These operators are illustrated in Table 5.1.

Table 5.1

	Example 1	*Example 2*
Original contents of accumulator:	01001011	10010010
After circular left shift:	10010110	00100101
After circular right shift:	10100101	01001001
After logical left shift:	10010110	00100100
After logical right shift:	00100101	01001001
After arithmetic right shift:	00100101	11001001

In some systems the shift operations may involve a special single-bit register called 'CARRY'. In circular shifts this register may be included in the loop, and in the others it is sometimes used to store the bit that drops off the end.

Arithmetic operations

Addition and subtraction on single words has already been mentioned in Chapter 3. In many cases (notably the handling of addresses) the range provided by single-word numbers is insufficient. Every microprocessor must therefore make provision for more complex arithmetic operations. The point at issue here is not the speed of these operations or the simplicity of using them, but whether they can be done at all. Three groups of operations will be mentioned as particularly important:

- multiple-length operations, with numbers that are long enough to need two (or more) words for their representation;
- multiplication and division;
- operations on numbers expressed as strings of decimal digits.

Branches and conditional branches

An essential aspect of a programmed system is that the sequence of its operations is not predetermined; instead, the system can make tests on the values of input variables and other quantities, and choose its course of action accordingly. A large variety of tests is commonly used. For example, a numerical quantity can be examined to see if it is zero, non-zero, negative or positive; or it can be compared against another quantity (which may be fixed or variable) to see if it is less, equal, not equal, or greater. The results of arithmetic operations can be checked for over-flow (that is, whether the 'true' result is outside the range of the numbers in the machine). Boolean variables can be tested for the values 'true' and 'false'.

In principle, all these tests can be provided by two jump instructions: an unconditional jump, and a jump that tests the sign bit of the accumulator. A check for zero can be made by subtracting 1 and testing whether the result changes sign. This restriction would lead to tedious and error-prone programming, and in practice every microprocessor offers a range of jump instructions that test different aspects of quantities in the system.

Array access

All the facilities considered so far have involved access to single, identified cells in the store. Many applications need tables, matrices, and other arrays of quantities, and refer to them in such a way that the precise element to be used at any instant cannot be determined in advance but depends on the current value of the input signal. Electronic engineers often use a similar approach, when they implement a family of complicated Boolean functions by putting the truth table into a read-only memory instead of designing a large amount of 'random' logic.

In a microprocessor system, tables could be used for price-lists, or for storing the details of peripheral devices, or for the coefficients of simultaneous equations involved in a control function, or for different moves to be followed in playing chess. Every microprocessor system should have some method of calculating and using the address of an element in a table, starting from the values of input variables that are not known in advance.

Stacks

The existence of a microprocessor is in one respect very like that of the author; it is full of interruptions. Some of these interruptions are voluntary, as when I stop writing and go to make myself a cup of tea; but others, like answering the telephone, are forced upon me. An interruption does not have much overall effect provided that I can eventually return exactly to the place, and to the frame of mind, in which I stopped writing.

A program in a microprocessor must also be capable of being interrupted, and again there are two causes: voluntary and involuntary. A voluntary interruption occurs when the program suspends its main stream of operations in order to carry out some subsidiary (but often vital) task. Such a task is called a *subroutine*. An involuntary interruption, or 'interrupt', often comes from a peripheral device that needs attention, and the section of program that provides that attention is called an 'interrupt routine'.

In most cases, interruptions can occur at several levels: while I am making my tea the telephone rings; while I am talking to the caller, the postman knocks at the door; while I am signing for the recorded delivery letter, my youngest child falls down the stairs . . .

Subroutines and interrupt routines generally use the accumulator, so provision must be made to store its previous contents while such a routine is running, and to restore it afterwards, when control is returned to the main program. It is also essential to remember the value of the program counter, so that the main program can be resumed at the correct point.

The early computers provided special fixed registers to retain this information, but it soon became clear that this mechanism could only deal with a single level of interruption. A more flexible device is the 'stack'. This is an array of registers with the property that any item of information that is sent there does not overwrite any previous item, but is placed 'on top', rather like a pile of cards in a tray. This means that a stack can hold an arbitrary number of items, and that they are retrieved in the reverse order to that in which they are inserted. (A stack is sometimes called a FILO — 'First In Last Out'.)

When a program is interrupted, the contents of the accumulator and program counter are sent to the stack, and the subroutine or interrupt routine that caused the interruption can safely be started. When the routine is complete, the original information can be retrieved from the stack. This system works for any number of levels of interruption, and

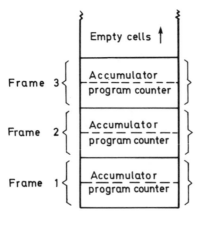

Accumulator and program counter of second-level interrupt routine, stacked when third-level interruption took place.

Accumulator and program counter of first-level interrupt routine, stacked when second-level interruption took place.

Accumulator and program counter of main program, stacked when first-level interruption took place.

Figure 5.2

allows the system to thread its way back, eventually, to the original program. At any moment the stack will hold a 'frame' for each active level of interruption, as shown in *Figure 5.2*.

Every microprocessor must have a stack, and it is highly desirable for there to be no practical limits on the number of items the stack may contain.

Peripheral controls

The prime purpose of most microprocessor systems is to communicate with peripheral devices of many kinds. To do this effectively, several features are needed:

- There should be no practical limit to the number of peripheral interfaces present.
- Communication with each device should be as simple as reading or writing to a store location.
- It should be possible to treat the peripheral interfaces as an array, and to select any one of them by using the current values of variable quantities.
- Any peripheral device should be able to signal its need for immediate attention by sending the system an *interrupt*, and making the microprocessor execute the appropriate interrupt routine. On the other hand, the interrupt routine should be protected against being interrupted itself, except by some other event of even greater urgency.

Desirable features

A microprocessor displaying the eight features described in the previous section would be programmable in every realistic situation, but the programs would often be slow, verbose and clumsy. The few extra properties described here can often make a substantial difference to the performance of the system.

Direct memory access

In Chapter 3 it was suggested that the address lines in the system bus are always controlled by the central processing unit. This means that the transfer of information between any two peripherals, or between a peripheral and the memory, must be organised by and through the CPU, and that every word to be moved requires (at least) an input and an output instruction.

For certain devices like disks or graphics display units this method is just not fast enough. One way of overcoming this problem is for the CPU to use tri-state drivers for the address lines; it can then relinquish control of the addresses and leave the two peripherals to organise the transfer by themselves. While the transfer is happening, the CPU can do nothing useful because it cannot fetch any instructions from the store; it must wait until it receives a signal to indicate that the transfer has ended. Nevertheless, the time lost is insignificant compared with the work that would have been needed to handle the transfer through the CPU.

Multiple registers

It is possible but often awkward to do everything through a single accumulator. Most microprocessors include a number of different registers within the CPU, some of them being double-length. Where many registers exist, it is important to have a full set of instructions for moving data between any pair; otherwise much of the advantage of the entire scheme is lost.

Immediate mode

Programs often refer to numerical or Boolean constants, like 0, 1, or 0FFH. In Chapter 3 these constants were given store locations of their own, and referred to by their addresses, thus:

```
        SUB ONE      ↑ SUBTRACT 1
        . . .
ONE:    1
```

A useful variant of many instructions that refer to the store is one in which the address is replaced by the operand itself (which must be constant). This would allow us to save store space by writing:

SUB #1 ↑ SUBTRACT 1. THE IMMEDIATE MODE IS INDICATED
        ↑ BY THE # SIGN

The immediate mode cannot, of course, be used with STORE, or jumps, or peripheral interface instructions; it would make no sense.

Short addresses

The first section of this chapter dealt with address spaces, and suggested that 16 bits was a reasonable minimum size for an address. This would mean that every address in a program must be 16 bits long. In practice, almost every instruction in a program contains an address, and it could save a good deal of store if the addresses could be compressed in some way — say to eight bits.

Many systems do offer compression; but this cannot be obtained without discarding some information. It is vital that the method of compression be well-designed so that the information thrown away is irrelevant in most cases, and can be easily retrieved if necessary. In a system that has been poorly thought out, short addresses can make a programmer's work very much harder.

Options

This final section deals with some of the features that can make a microprocessor especially suitable for particular applications.

Parity detection

If a microprocessor is used for communication and handles characters received from remote places, much of its work will lie in checking the accuracy of transmission. This will involve calculating the parity of every character received. This can be done in three ways:

- by counting the 1's (this is time-consuming);
- by table-lookup (this is expensive on store);
- by special hardware within the CPU.

Processors that have parity-checking hardware are at an advantage in this particular area.

Multiplication and division

These operations, which are useful in numerical control, are sometimes provided as built-in instructions. A microprocessor that does not have them must do multiplication and division by repeated addition (or subtraction) and shifting, and this is very much slower.

Indirection

In an ordinary store reference instruction, such as

LOAD   25

the address indicates the cell that holds the operand to be fetched. If indirection is used, the cell holds the *address* of the operand. For example, if cell 25 held the number 17, the instruction

LOAD   IND (25)   ↑ HERE IND SPECIFIES INDIRECTION

would load the contents of cell 17.

Indirection is chiefly useful in complex programs, but is difficult to use correctly. Many programmers avoid this facility if they can.

6

Introduction to the Motorola 6800

The Motorola 6800 is one of the most widely used microprocessors in industry, and will serve as the main example of machine architecture. The general principles are applicable to most other devices, and a comparison of the detailed features of the 6800 and one of its competing microprocessors is given in Chapter 10.

Motorola 6800 architecture

The Motorola 6800 microprocessor is available in several variants, which differ in speed and in the amount of on-board storage carried. From the programmer's point of view, all the types are identical, and the physical differences will not be considered here. *Figure 6.1* shows the system as the programmer might see it.

The CPU is driven by a clock pulse generator, running (typically) at 500 kHz. It is connected to the other components by the system bus, which has 16 address lines, eight data lines, two interrupt lines, and various signal lines used for control and synchronisation.

The other components include a block of random-access memory, a block of read-only memory, and any number of peripheral interface devices — numbered PC#1 to PC#4 in the diagram.

The word length is eight bits, and the address space is 2^{16} or 65 536 words. Every component except the CPU occupies a distinct position in the address space; that is, each block of store and every peripheral has its own unique address or group of addresses. The CPU can access any component by broadcasting the address of that component on the system bus, because each component is normally fitted with an address response mechanism to ensure that it alone responds when its own address appears on the bus.

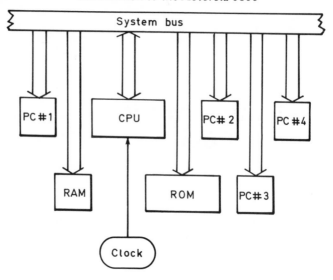

Figure 6.1

The arrangement of devices within the address space is extremely flexible. The only constraints are:

- There *must* be some ROM in the last eight locations FFF8 to FFFF. This is needed for starting the system and handling interrupts.
- There are advantages in placing RAM in the *first* 256 words 0000 to 00FF. (The precise reason will be discussed in Chapter 7.)

A typical address map is shown in *Figure 6.2*.

The address response mechanism for a particular 16-bit address is a somewhat cumbersome network, involving a 16-input AND operation and up to 16 inverters. In smaller systems the designer may sometimes use his freedom to position peripheral interfaces in such a way as to make response very much easier. Consider a system somewhat like the one in *Figure 6.2*, with 1024 words of RAM, 512 words of ROM, and five peripheral interfaces. Suppose that the bits in the address are numbered a_{15} to a_0. If the RAM occupies the lowest 1024 words of the address space, any address within the RAM will have bits a_{15} to a_{10} equal to zero. Similarly, any ROM address will have bits a_{15} to a_9 set to 1.

The designer can reassign peripheral interface addresses in order to exploit this regularity. He might, for example, assign one of the address lines a_{14} to a_{10} to each interface, and use that line (and a 0 on a_{15}) as the sole selection criterion. The 'a_{14}' interface could then be selected

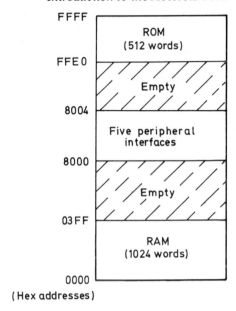

Figure 6.2

by the combination ($a_{15} = 0$, $a_{14} = 1$), regardless of the other address lines. This could be done by one NAND gate and one inverter; or it might be possible to use a chip with independent 'chip select' and 'not chip select' inputs, and to connect it directly to the system bus without any explicit address-selection mechanism at all.

Of course this method of discriminating addresses would place constraints on the programmer, who would now be *told* precisely what address to use for each peripheral device, and warned that incorrect addresses might lead to a catastrophic failure of the whole system because two or more interfaces had responded at the same time and burned out their tri-state bus drivers. For example, this would occur in response to the address '0110000000000000', which would activate both the 'a_{14}' and 'a_{13}' devices.

The Motorola 6800 order code

The complete order code for the 6800 microprocessor is given in full in Appendix 2. At this point, however, only a subset will be discussed; most of the remainder will be introduced gradually over the next two chapters.

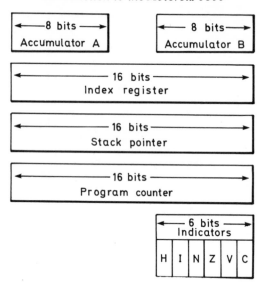

Figure 6.3

The order code assumes a CPU with registers arranged as shown in *Figure 6.3*. (The index register, stack pointer and indicators H and I will not be of concern till later.)

The two *accumulators* A and B are each eight bits long; they can both be used for most operations. The *program counter* keeps a record of the location of the next instruction to be obeyed, and is advanced every time an instruction is fetched from the store. Since this instruction may in principle be taken from any position in the address space, the program counter is necessarily 16 bits long.

The *indicators* are used to record certain facts about the result of the most recent operation. Each is a single binary digit. In general:

N records whether the result was negative (that is, whether the most significant bit was a '1').

Z records whether the result was precisely zero.

V records whether the result (treated as a signed number) was too large to be held in eight bits and is therefore represented wrongly.

C is used for two purposes. In addition and subtraction, it records whether a carry (or a borrow) appears at the left-hand end of the sum. In shifts, it is used to supply and record various digits.

To give an example, consider an instruction in which 5 was subtracted from 3, giving −2:

```
00000011
00000101  −
─────────
11111110
```

N would be set *true*, because the result is negative.

Z would be set *false*, because the result is not zero.

V would be set *false*, because the result (regarded as a signed number) is correct.

C would be set *true*, because an outstanding 'borrow' appears at the left of the sum.

The reader is warned that for a few instructions the indicators are used in a slightly different way.

The 6800 has a rich set of instructions − that is, there are far more than are strictly necessary to write programs. They are arranged in families, and presented in tabular fashion below. At this point the reader should go through the tables once or twice, but need not make any attempt to learn the material by heart; the details will very quickly impress themselves on his mind as soon as he begins to write real programs.

Addressless instructions on accumulator A

All the instructions in this group (shown in Table 6.1) work directly on accumulator A, and need no other operand from the store. The indicators are set to record the result of each operation.

Each instruction in this group occupies one word in the store, and takes two clock pulses to be executed. With a 500 kHz clock, this is 4 microseconds.

In Tables 6.1 to 6.4, the results in the indicators are coded as follows:

R Always set to *false* or 0.

S Always set to *true* or 1.

↕ Set according to result of the main operation.

   Unaffected.

1 V set if result = 10000000. This would happen if the number negated is 10000000, or −128, of which the true complement is out of range.

2 C set if the result is 0.

4 V set if Acc A = 10000000 before execution of DEC A.

5 V set if Acc A = 01111111 before execution of INC A.

6 V set if N and C are different after the operation.

Table 6.1

Mnemonic	Result in				Explanation
	N	Z	V	C	
CLR A	R	S	R	R	Sets Acc A = 0.
COM A	↕	↕	R	S	Complements Acc A (i.e. changes all the bits).
NEG A	↕	↕	1	2	Negates Acc A (i.e. subtracts it from 0).
DEC A	↕	↕	4	.	Subtracts 1 from Acc A.
INC A	↕	↕	5	.	Adds 1 to Acc A.
ROL A	↕	↕	6	.	Rotates Acc A one place left, including C in the loop.
ROR A	↕	↕	6	.	Rotates Acc A one place right, including C in the loop.
ASL A	↕	↕	6	.	Logical left shift of Acc A with left-most bit sent to C.
ASR A	↕	↕	6	.	Arithmetic right shift of Acc A with right-most bit sent to C.
LSR A	↕	↕	6	.	Logical right shift of Acc A, with right-most bit sent to C.
TST A	↕	↕	R	R	Sets N and Z to current value of Acc A, without affecting this value itself.

Addressless instructions on accumulator B

A set of instructions identical to the ones shown in Table 6.1 is available for Accumulator B.

Operations between accumulators

This group of instructions (Table 6.2) uses both accumulators. It will be noticed that the operations are not symmetrical, accumulator A being more privileged. These operations again take two clock pulses each.

Table 6.2

Mnemonic	Result in				Explanation
	N	Z	V	C	
ABA	↕	↕	↕	↕	Adds B to A.
CBA	↕	↕	↕	↕	Sets indicators according to A−B. Does not change A or B.
SBA	↕	↕	↕	↕	Subtracts B from A.
TAB	↕	↕	R	.	Copies A to B.
TBA	↕	↕	R	.	Copies B to A.

Operations involving an accumulator and an operand

This group of functions (Table 6.3) provides arithmetic and logic operations. Each function exists in several modes:

- It may specify either accumulator A or accumulator B.
- The operand may either take from a specified address in the store, or it can be the address part of the instruction itself. If a store address is used, the instruction is said to be in *extended* mode. It occupies three consecutive words, as follows:

Function	Most significant half of address	Least significant half of address

  8 bits   8 bits   8 bits

As they have 16 bits of address, instructions in extended mode can refer to any location in the store. With one exception, they take four clock pulses to be executed. Instructions that contain their own operands are said to be in *immediate* mode. They are executed in two clock pulses, and occupy two consecutive words, thus:

Function	Operand

  8 bits   8 bits

Table 6.3

Mnemonic	Result in				Explanation
	N	Z	V	C	
ADD	↕	↕	↕	↕	Adds operand to accumulator.
ADC	↕	↕	↕	↕	Adds operand + C (0 or 1) to accumulator.
AND	↕	↕	↕	↕	ANDs operand with accumulator.
BIT	↕	↕	R	.	Sets indicators to result of ANDing accumulator and operand. Does not change accumulator.
CMP	↕	↕	↕	↕	Sets indicator to result of subtracting operand from accumulator. Does not change accumulator.
EOR	↕	↕	R	.	Exclusive ORs operand with accumulator.
LDA	↕	↕	R	.	Loads operand to accumulator, destroying its previous contents.
ORA	↕	↕	R	.	Inclusive ORs operand with accumulator.
SUB	↕	↕	↕	↕	Subtracts operand from accumulator.
SBC	↕	↕	↕	↕	Subtracts (operand + C) from accumulator.
STA	↕	↕	R	.	Stores accumulator in specified memory cell.

● Instructions in this group also have two other modes, *direct* and *indexed*, discussion of which is deferred.

In assembly language, each of the mnemonics in this group must be followed by an A or a B to indicate the selected accumulator, a comma, and an address or an immediate operand, indicated by a # sign. For example:

ADD A, #3   ↑ ADD NUMBER 3 TO ACC A
SUB B, 1000   ↑ SUBTRACT CONTENTS OF CELL 1000 FROM
                  ACCUMULATOR B

The STA instruction (store) has no immediate form — it would not make sense. In extended mode, STA takes five clock pulses.

Operations directly on store locations

The instructions in this group (Table 6.4) do not affect the accumulators at all, but operate directly on the contents of selected cells in the store. Each instruction is three words long, and is arranged as follows:

Function	Most significant half of address	Least significant half of address
8 bits	8 bits	8 bits

The instructions each take six clock pulses to execute, and are closely analogous in effect to those listed in Table 6.1.

Table 6.4

Mnemonic	Result in				Explanation
	N	Z	V	C	
CLR	R	S	R	R	Clear store location to zero.
COM	↕	↕	R	S	Complement.
NEG	↕	↕	1	2	Negate (subtract from 0).
DEC	↕	↕	4	.	Decrement (subtract 1).
INC	↕	↕	5	.	Increment (add 1).
ROL	↕	↕	6	↕	Circular left shift.
ROR	↕	↕	6	↕	Circular right shift.
ASL	↕	↕	6	↕	Logical left shift.
ASR	↕	↕	6	↕	Arithmetical right shift.
LSR	↕	↕	6	↕	Logical right shift.
TST	↕	↕	R	R	Set N and Z according to contents of store location.

Branch instructions

The final group of instructions in this chapter is concerned with jumps, or transfers of control. Jumps may either be *unconditional*, always causing transfers of control, or they may depend on the setting of one of the indicator bits N, Z, V or C.

Ordinary branch instructions take four clock pulses to be executed, and occupy two machine words, as follows:

Function	Offset

8 'bits   8 bits

The offset is a *signed* eight-bit number in two's complement notation; it therefore has the range −128 to +127. Instead of indicating the absolute address of the next instruction, it shows how many cells to move forward or backward from the current position. This arrangement takes advantage of the observed fact that most jumps in programs span only a small number of words. Each jump instruction can be written using only two words instead of the three that would be needed if the destination address were stated in full.

As to the actual details of the instruction, it is worth remembering that branches are executed in the following sequence:

1:   The instruction is fetched into the CPU.
2:   The program counter is advanced by two.
3:   The test is made. If it is satisfied
4:   The offset is added to the program counter.

It can be deduced that this allows jumps of up to 129 cells forward, or 126 cells backward, from the location of the branch instruction itself.

In practice, programs can be written with symbolic labels and the assembler will calculate and set up the offsets automatically. The assembler will print a warning if the destination address is beyond the range of a branch.

Some of the branch instructions are given in Table 6.5. None of them affects the condition codes.

To allow for the possibility of jumping to *any* address, a single jump instruction is provided with the mnemonic JMP and a 16-bit absolute address. Its layout is:

Function	Most significant half of address	Least significant half of address

8 bits   8 bits   8 bits

Table 6.5

Mnemonic	Comments
BRA	Unconditional branch.
BCC	Jump if C clear.
BCS	Jump if C set.
BVC	Jump if V clear.
BVS	Jump if V set.
BNE	Jump if Z clear (i.e. result not zero).
BEQ	Jump if Z set (i.e. result = zero).
BPL	Jump if N clear (i.e. result $\geq$ 0).
BMI	Jump if N set (i.e. result $<$ 0).

Some sample programs

This section provides some sample illustrations of the order code we have just described.

Multiplication

Where the operands are known to be very small, multiplication can be done by repeated addition. The following fragment of program will multiply the contents of the cells with symbolic names X and Y, placing the product in Z. The product will be correct if X is zero or positive, and X.Y $\leq$ 127. The program should be compared with that on page 24.

```
           CLR   B              ↑ CLEAR B
           LDA   A, X           ↑ LOAD X
LOOP:      DEC   A              ↑ SUBTRACT 1
           BEQ   CONTINUE       ↑ OUT IF RESULT = 0
           ADD   B, Y           ↑ ADD Y TO B
           BRA   LOOP           ↑ JUMP BACK
CONTINUE:  STA   B, Z           ↑ STORE RESULT
```

This is a very restricted form of multiplication, since, in general, the product of two eight-bit numbers is a 16-bit quantity. A more general algorithm, which is a version of 'school' multiplication and works for all positive numbers, is as follows:

Product (top half)		Product (bottom half)

Multiplicand	

Multiplier		C

Counter	

To begin, the multiplicand and the multiplier are placed in certain registers, a counter register is loaded with the number of bits in each word (eight in this case) and the product register (which must be twice the size of the operands) is cleared to zero.

The multiplication takes eight stages. At each stage, the multiplier is shifted one place to the right. This moves the (current) least significant bit into C, where it can be tested. If it is a 1, the multiplicand is added to the top half of the product register. If the bit from the multiplier is 0, the addition is omitted. Then, in either case, the product register—all 16 bits of it — is shifted one place to the right.

The first few stages of the multiplication of 87 (01010111) by 29 (00011101) are shown below. The reader should convince himself that the algorithm does indeed generate the correct double-length product, by working through the remaining five stages:

```
Start:            00000000  00000000                        (P)
                  01010111                                  (M'cand)
                  00011101                                  (M'plier)
                  00001000                                  (Counter)
After 1 stage:    00101011  10000000                        (P)
                  01010111                                  (M'cand)
                  00001110  (1)     ('Add and shift')       (M'plier)
                  00000111                                  (Counter)
After 2 stages:   00010101  11000000                        (P)
                  01010111                                  (M'cand)
                  00000111  (0)     ('Shift')               (M'plier)
                  00000110                                  (Counter)
After 3 stages:   00110110  01100000                        (P)
                  01010111                                  (M'cand)
                  00000011  (1)     ('Add and shift')       (M'plier)
                  00000101                                  (Counter)
```

The final result is 00001001 11011011. This is a 16-bit number with denary equivalent 2523, which is indeed (87 × 29).

So far the algorithm has been presented in abstract form. The next stage is to plan a program by assigning specific cells and registers to the various quantities.

The accumulators in the CPU are easier to reach and manipulate than cells in the store, so in an ideal machine we would place all the variable quantities in accumulators. There are, however, only two accumulators in the 6800, so a compromise must be made.

There is no direct way of adding quantities to cells in the store, so one obvious candidate for an accumulator is the most significant half of the product. All the operations on the other quantities — shifting and decrementing — *can* be done directly on store locations, so the other quantity to be held in an accumulator can be chosen freely. One suitable choice is the multiplier.

One point of difficulty is the shifting of the product, which is a 16-bit quantity. Clearly it must be shifted in two halves, and the link between them, which ensures that a digit is moved from the right of the most significant half to the left of the least significant half, can be arranged through C. Suppose the bits of the product at any time are:

a_{15} a_{14} a_{13} a_{12} a_{11} a_{10} a_9 a_8 a_7 a_6 a_5 a_4 a_3 a_2 a_1 a_0

Top half   Bottom half

The shift can be made in two stages:

● Shift the top half *logically*. It will be left as:

0 a_{15} a_{14} a_{13} a_{12} a_{11} a_{10} a_9

a_8 will be left in C.

● Shift the bottom half cyclically. This will move a_8 in at the left, and leave:

a_8 a_7 a_6 a_5 a_4 a_3 a_2 a_1

The a_0 now in C can be ignored; the double-length shift has been accomplished.

The program that follows assumes the following:
Multiplier in cell X
Multiplicand in cell Y
Product to be delivered in PH (top half)
                        and PL (bottom half)
COUNT is a work-space
X, Y, PH, PL and COUNT are all store locations.

During the program, the top half of the product is to be held in accumulator A and the multiplier in accumulator B.

```
BEGIN:   LDA  A, #8        ↑ INITIALISE COUNT
         STA  A, COUNT
         CLR  PL           ↑ SET PRODUCT TO ZERO
         CLR  A
         LDA  B, X         ↑ LOAD MULTIPLIER
LOOP:    LSR  B            ↑ SHIFT BOTTOM BIT OF
                           ↑ M'PLIER INTO C
         BCC  SHIFT        ↑ JUMP IF C = 0
         ADD  A, Y         ↑ ADD M'CAND TO ACC A
SHIFT:   LSR  A            ↑ SHIFT 16-BIT PRODUCT
         ROR  PL
         DEC  COUNT        ↑ REDUCE COUNT BY 1
         BNE  LOOP         ↑ JUMP BACK IF NOT ZERO
         STA  A, PH        ↑ RECORD TOP HALF OF
                           ↑ PRODUCT
         . . .             ↑ NEXT PART OF PROGRAM
         . . .
COUNT:   0
PH:      0
PL:      0
X:       (multiplier)
Y:       (multiplicand)
```

As an exercise, the reader should verify that, if the multiplier contains four 1's, the multiplication takes 230 clock pulses or 460 microseconds.

Calculation of parity

A program that handles alphanumeric data often needs to check on the *parity* of a character (see Chapter 2). The following program begins with a character in accumulator A, and ends with the parity of the character indicated in accumulator B as 1 = odd, 0 = even.

```
      CLR  B         ↑ CLEAR ACC B
YY:   LSR  A         ↑ SHIFT LOW BIT OF A INTO C
      BCC  ZZ        ↑ JUMP IF ZERO
      EOR  B, #1     ↑ CHANGE LOW BIT OF B
ZZ:   TST  A         ↑ TEST A,
      BNE  YY        ↑ JUMP BACK IF ANY MORE 1's LEFT
      . . . *
```

In the worst case (all 1's) this fragment would take 120 clock pulses or 240 μs. The average time (with four 1's and four 0's) would be a little over half this figure.

Fire alarm system

A house is to be fitted with a fire alarm system, with four main components:

- Heat detectors in all the main rooms. Each detector is a switch actuated by a bi-metallic strip. Under normal conditions the switch is closed, but opens when the temperature exceeds a preset limit.
- An alarm bell in the house.
- A remote alarm in the nearby fire station.
- A control panel.

The operational requirements are as follows:

- If any heat detector registers, even momentarily, the local alarm bell is to sound continuously, and a tell-tale light is to be illuminated on the control panel.
- If any *two* heat detectors register (not necessarily at the same moment), the remote alarm must be turned on as well as the local alarm. The remote alarm must also be turned on in response to a 'call fire brigade' button.
- Once activated, the alarms must continue to sound until the 'reset' button is pressed.
- The system must have a 'self-test' mode, which verifies that there are no obvious faults (like lack of power).

A sketch of the control panel is given in *Figure 6.4*. Circles represent lights, and squares stand for pushbutton switches. The upper row indicates where (if anywhere) the fire has been detected, and the lights marked 'OK' and 'Fault' show the results of the test. The 'fire service called' light is a repeater for the remote alarm.

The detectors, control panel and alarm bells are connected to the microcomputer through four interfaces arranged as shown in *Figure 6.5*.

The connectors and 'test' button are connected as shown in *Figure 6.6*. Normally, when the 'test' button is not pressed, the lower sides of the head detector switches are earthed. This ensures that the 'detector' signal from each one is low unless the heat-sensitive switch is opened.

The 'test' button operates two ganged switches. The first provides a 'high' test signal, and the second connects the lower sides of the heat

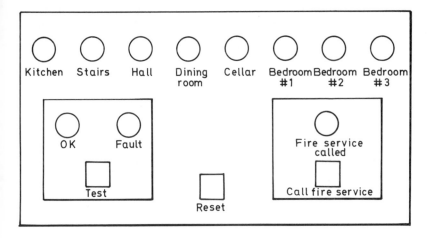

Figure 6.4

detectors to a high voltage, ensuring that the detect signals all go 'high' unless the system is badly defective.

The system is required to take permanent action on the basis of momentary signals from the heat detectors. It therefore accumulates these signals in a register that is initially set to zero, and continuously ORed with the word of detector signals. This word is called the 'alarm accumulator'.

Address	Layout							
F000: Detectors	Kitchen	Stairs	Hall	Dining room	Cellar	Bed #1	Bed #2	Bed#3
F001: Buttons on control panel						Test	Reset	Call fire service
F002: Tell-tale lamps	Kitchen	Stairs	Hall	Dining room	Cellar	Bed #1	Bed#2	Bed#3
F003: Test lamps and alarm					OK	Faulty	Remote alarm	Local alarm

Figure 6.5

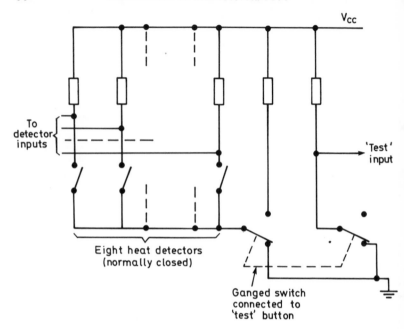

Figure 6.6

The mechanism of the alarm system can be shown as a network of four states (*Figure 6.7*). State 1 is the 'ready' state, entered when the system is first started, or following a reset. In this state, the system continually monitors all the inputs and moves to another state if there is any change.

State 2 is for testing the system. In this state, all detectors should return a 1. The system continually inspects them and lights up the 'OK' or 'Fault' lamp accordingly. It is of course understood that the system must also be faulty if neither light is illuminated. State 2 returns control to state 1 when the 'test' button is released.

State 3 is the 'local alarm' state, entered when an alarm has been detected. If only one detector has registered, the system rings the local bell, and continues to monitor all the inputs except 'test', eventually moving to another state as may be appropriate.

State 4 is the 'general alarm' state, and is only entered if (a) more than one detector has registered, or (b) the fire brigade is called explicitly. The state sounds both local and remote alarms, and can only be stopped by the 'reset' button.

67

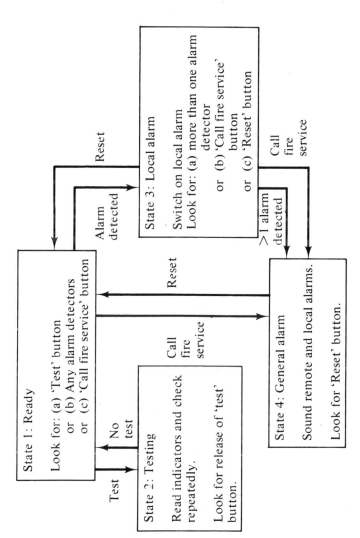

Figure 6.7

The control program for the alarm system is shown below. Each state is represented by its own group of instructions, and transfers between states are effected by jump instructions.

The program is curious in that it needs no RAM at all. The 'alarm accumulator' is kept in accumulator B, and the current state is implicit in the value of the program counter.

```
TITLE "FIRE ALARM SYSTEM"
DETECTORS:=  ?F000          ↑ ADDRESSES OF PERI-
                            ↑ PHERALS
BUTTONS:=    ?F001
TELLTALE:=   ?F002
ALARMS:=     ?F003
. = 0                       ↑ CODE STARTS AT WORD 0
STATE1:  CLR TELLTALE       ↑ CLEAR TELLTALE LIGHTS
         CLR ALARMS         ↑ AND ANY ALARMS STILL ON
         CLR B              ↑ CLEAR ALARM ACCUMU-
                            ↑ LATOR
LOOPA:   LDA A, BUTTONS     ↑ READ PANEL BUTTONS
         BIT A, #4          ↑ TEST FOR "TEST"
         BNE STATE2         ↑ TO STATE 2 IF PRESSED
         BIT A, #1          ↑ TEST FOR "CALL FIRE
                            ↑ SERVICE"
         BNE STATE4         ↑ TO STATE 4 IF PRESSED
         ORA B, DETECTORS   ↑ LOOK AT DETECTORS
         BEQ LOOPA          ↑ BACK TO LOOP A IF NO-
                            ↑ THING FOUND
         BRA STATE3         ↑ OTHERWISE GO TO STATE 3
STATE2:  LDA A, DETECTORS   ↑ READ DETECTORS
         CMP A, #?FF        ↑ TEST IF ALL ONES
         BEQ XX             ↑ JUMP IF SO
         LDA, A, #4         ↑ ELSE SWITCH ON
         STA A, ALARMS      ↑ "FAULTY" LIGHT
         BRA YY
XX:      LDA A, #8          ↑ ALL ONES FOUND. SWITCH
         STA A, ALARMS      ↑ ON "OK" LIGHT
YY:      LDA, A, BUTTONS    ↑ LOOK AT "TEST" BUTTON
         BIT A, #4
         BNE STATE2         ↑ STAY IN STATE 2 IF STILL
                            ↑ PRESSED
         BRA STATE1         ↑ ELSE RETURN TO STATE 1
STATE3:  LDA A, #1          ↑ SOUND LOCAL ALARM
         STA A, ALARMS
         LDA A, BUTTONS     ↑ LOOK AT BUTTONS
```

```
            BIT A, #2            ↑ RETURN TO STATE 1
            BNE STATE 1          ↑ IF "RESET" PRESSED
            BIT A, #1            ↑ GO TO STATE 4. IF
            BNE STATE2           ↑ "CALL FIRE SERVICE"
                                 ↑ PRESSED
            ORA B, DETECTORS     ↑ ILLUMINATE TELLTALE
            STA B, TELLTALE      ↑ LIGHTS
            TBA                  ↑ COPY B TO A
ZZ:         LSR A                ↑ SEE IF MORE THAN 1 BIT
            BCC ZZ               ↑ SET IN A. IF NOT, STAY
            BEQ STATE3           ↑ IN STATE 3
            BRA STATE4           ↑ OTHERWISE GO TO STATE 4
                                 ↑ THE READER IS INVITED TO
                                 ↑ PUZZLE OUT THIS SEQUENCE
                                 ↑ BY HIMSELF, BY TRACING
                                 ↑ IF NECESSARY
STATE4:     LDA A, #3            ↑ SOUND BOTH ALARMS
            STA A, ALARMS
            ORA B, DETECTORS     ↑ KEEP TELLTALE LIGHTS UP
                                 ↑ TO DATE
            STA B, TELLTALE
            LDA A, BUTTONS       ↑ LOOK FOR "RESET"
            BIT A, #2
            BNE STATE1           ↑ BACK TO STATE 1 IF
                                 ↑ PRESSED
            BRA STATE4           ↑ ELSE STAY IN STATE 4
START       STATE1
```

Some programming techniques

Routines and subroutines

One of the most difficult problems in engineering is the control of complexity. Most machines (such as typewriters, television sets or cars) consist of hundreds or thousands of parts and need manuals several inches thick to describe their construction. Aircraft carriers and nuclear power stations are so complicated that no one person can ever hope to understand the entire design in detail.

There is one category of machine for which this problem does not arise. Some devices, like pruning-shears or bicycle pumps, are so simple that the purpose of each part is immediately obvious. Such a machine can be completely 'understood' without any noticeable effort, because the number of distinct ideas involved is small, and the human mind can grasp them all at the same time.

The only method that allows this simplicity of approach to be applied to more complex machines is the principle of hierarchical design. This method splits the design of a system into a number of levels, each one with increasing detail, until ultimately the individual physical components are reached.

To illustrate the method, consider a team designing a new car. The head designer will think of the car as having only three components: engine, transmission and body. His perception of these parts will be in global terms; he will see the engine as a unit having certain characteristics such as a torque-speed curve, a maximum power output, a certain weight, a range of fuel consumption and a particular production cost. The chief of the team will rightly not be interested in practical details like the dimensions of the gudgeon pins; instead, he will delegate the actual job of designing the engine to a member of his group.

The sub-division of the design is likely to go further. The designer in charge of the engine must decide on its layout and main dimensions, but he will probably delegate the detailed design of the carburettor, ignition and other sub-systems to junior colleagues. Only at this level will work begin on the design and selection of actual physical components, like float chambers and sparking plugs. A diagram of this design method is shown in *Figure 7.1*.

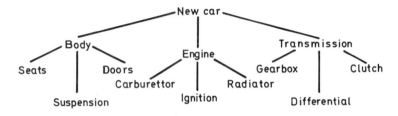

Figure 7.1

The hierarchic approach has several advantages, including that of allowing many people to work on the design at the same time. Its chief benefit, however, is that it permits each member of the team to think in terms of only a few concepts at any time. These concepts need not be — and usually will not be — elementary, but will refer to sub-systems, each of which is seen as a complete machine by a designer lower in the hierarchy. This is no disadvantage, since the limiting factor in understanding a system is not the complexity of any idea involved, but simply the *number* of different ideas to be manipulated at the same time.

The method of hierarchical design is of great value in programming. The programs presented in Chapters 1 to 6 were all exceedingly simple, so that they could be understood even without any hierarchic structure; they were on the intellectual level of pruning-shears or bicycle pumps. The hierarchic method makes it possible to write programs that are complex enough to handle realistic problems, and that yet remain comprehensible to their designers. The method can be used even when all the programming is being done by one person; all that is necessary is for the designer to play successively the parts of the chief designer and the other members of the team.

The reader is solemnly warned that attempts to write large programs (i.e. any program with more than about 100 statements) without using the hierarchic method will always end in disaster. Such programs will take much longer than expected to work at all, and then they will still contain serious errors. This unpleasant fact contradicts the intuition of many people who have experience of writing small programs successfully; it is by no means easy to see that methods that work with toy programs cannot be scaled up.

Most electronic engineers are familiar with the notion of sub-assemblies. To be successful, a sub-assembly should have five properties:

- It must do a precisely defined job.
- It must fit in to the machine of which it is a part; that is, it must present the correct interfaces to the other sub-assemblies to which it is connected.
- It must not be allowed to interfere with the working of any other sub-assembly (e.g. by electrical noise or heat).
- It should preferably be capable of being run when it is removed from the system, and plugged in to a simple test rig.
- If complicated, it should be divisible into sub-sub-assemblies as far as necessary.

In a program a sub-assembly is called a 'routine'. A routine is a self-contained sequence of instructions that fulfils a precisely defined purpose. For example, a system that handles characters arriving over data transmission lines will have a routine to test their parity, or a system that maintains a digital display may well have a routine to convert numbers from binary to denary and send the corresponding characters to the display device.

Before it can be written, a routine needs an *exact* specification. This might be, for example:

'Routine PARITY is entered with an eight-bit character in accumulator A. It delivers the parity of this character (as 1 = odd, 0 = even) in accumulator B. The contents of accumulator A are destroyed.'

or:

'Routine DISPLAY is entered with a binary number supposed to be in the range ?00 to ?63 (0 to 99 decimal) in accumulator A. It converts it to decimal form, and displays the corresponding digits on seven-segment LEDs connected to locations ?F100 (tens digit) and ?F101 (units digit). If the number in accumulator A should exceed 99 the routine displays two minus signs; this is an error indication. The routine destroys the contents of accumulator A and of the index register.'

These descriptions define the purpose of the routine, and also contain information about the way the inputs are presented and the results returned. This information is needed to ensure that the routine fits properly with other parts of the program. The reader will see that the description of the routine's job is inseparable from that of its interface.

Routines are the components of a program, and it is common for one routine to invoke, or to call upon the services of, another one at a lower level. It is vital that the routines be prevented from interfering with one another. The greatest danger is caused by unintended use of the same store location. Consider a routine that stores a Very Important Quantity in location 0, and then invokes a lower-level routine, which then uses location 0 as a temporary work area – perhaps for storing a counter. The VIQ will be spoiled or *corrupted* whenever the low-level routine is used, and the high-level routine will produce the wrong result. This design mistake is not serious if location 0 is corrupted *every* time round the program, since the error will show up at the first test and can easily be corrected at that stage. It becomes harder to find and potentially dangerous if the lower routine is only sometimes called or, if called, it only sometimes uses location 0. The fault will then be intermittent, and may not even be noticed until the system is already in service.

A method of avoiding this danger is to ensure that every routine uses its own private area of store for workspace. One way of doing this is to give each routine a distinctive name, and then to label all the items used by the routine with names derived from the routine name itself. For example a routine called TX would contain items labelled TXA, TXB . . .

A routine is just a sequence of instructions and must be embedded as part of a larger sequence. It is not really independent of its environment. Thus a program that needed to calculate a parity in two different contexts would need two identical copies of the necessary routine.

A routine can be made independent by casting it as a *subroutine*. A subroutine is a routine that can be invoked or 'called' from any part of a program and that has the ability eventually to return control to the place whence it was called.

In general terms this can always be done by storing the *address* of the instruction to return to, for the duration of the subroutine. When the subroutine ends, it executes a jump to that address, which may be different on different occasions.

The 6800 has a special mechanism for calling subroutines and returning to the main sequence of instructions. The instruction JSR ('Jump to SubRoutine') transfers control to the beginning of a subroutine, but first it preserves the eventual return address (which is that of the instruction following the JSR). The format of the instruction is:

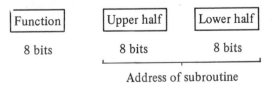

The complementary instruction is RTS ('ReTurn from Subroutine'). It is placed at the end of a subroutine, and simply jumps back to the address preserved by the JSR that called the subroutine in the first place. RTS needs no explicit address and is therefore a one-byte instruction.

Below is part of a program for message switching. Routine A is responsible for receiving characters that arrive on data transmission lines and checking their parity for possible errors. Routine B is in charge of transmitting characters to a remote destination. Before each character is transmitted, its parity must be checked and adjusted if necessary to make it even. Both routines therefore need a 'parity' function, which is provided as a subroutine. The RTS instruction returns control to AX when the parity subroutine was called by routine A, but to BX when it was called by B.

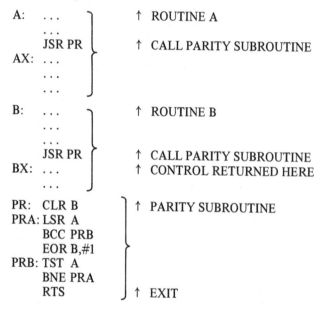

```
A:   ...              ↑ ROUTINE A
     ...
     JSR PR           ↑ CALL PARITY SUBROUTINE
AX:  ...
     ...
     ...

B:   ...              ↑ ROUTINE B
     ...
     ...
     JSR PR           ↑ CALL PARITY SUBROUTINE
BX:  ...              ↑ CONTROL RETURNED HERE
     ...

PR:  CLR B            ↑ PARITY SUBROUTINE
PRA: LSR A
     BCC PRB
     EOR B,#1
PRB: TST A
     BNE PRA
     RTS              ↑ EXIT
```

There is of course no need to label the instructions following JSRs. This was only done in the example as an aid to clarity.

The actual storage of the return address is done with a stack, in general accordance with the principle described on page 45. The stack is kept in RAM, and may be placed anywhere in the address space.

The current 'free' location in the stack is preserved by a 16-bit CPU register called the 'stack pointer'. The stack grows towards location 0, so every time a subroutine is called, the return address (which is 16 bits long) is recorded in the pair of cells indicated by this stack pointer, and the pointer is *reduced* by 2. This method allows subroutines to be nested to an arbitrary depth, so long as enough stack space is available.

In any program that is to use subroutines, the designer must allocate space for the stack. The number of cells needed is strictly twice the number of subroutine 'levels', but it is always wise to allow a substantial extra number in case any new subroutines are ever used at a later date. A stack of 50 cells is enough for most programs. It can be declared, amongst other data items, by a sequence like:

```
STACKBOTTOM:   0  ↑ THIS DECLARES THE LOWEST CELL IN
                  ↑ THE STACK
. = . +48         ↑ THIS RESERVES 48 CELLS BY MOVING
                  ↑ THE CURRENT POSITION OF . ON BY 48
STACKTOP:   0     ↑ THIS DECLARES THE HIGHEST, OR 50TH
                  ↑ CELL IN THE STACK
```

Before calling any subroutine, the program must set the stack pointer to indicate the beginning of the stack. This is done by the instruction LDS, which has immediate and extended modes, and is usually the first instruction in any program. For example:

```
BEGIN: LDS  #STACKTOP    ↑ LOAD TOP ADDRESS OF STACK
```

Note that since the stack grows towards zero the pointer must initially indicate the *top*, not the *bottom*, of the stack area.

Experience shows that, in general, subroutines should be less than 40 instructions long. Any task that seems to take more than this amount of code should be divided into two or more subroutines. This approach means that large programs have a well-developed hierarchical structure with many levels. The code at the higher levels consists mainly of subroutine calls:

```
. . .
JSR  BODY
JSR  ENGINE
JSR  TRANSMISSION
. . .
```

High-precision arithmetic

Many applications of microprocessors need arithmetic to be carried out to a higher precision than the eight binary digits in a single word of the 6800. For example, analogue biological signals such as those from electrocardiographs are normally converted to binary with 12-digit precision, and addresses, which sometimes have to be added and subtracted, are a full 16 digits long.

On the 6800, high-precision quantities can be represented by using two or more words to hold all the binary digits. For example, a 20-bit number could be held in three adjacent words, arranged as follows:

0 0 0 0	X X X X		X X X X X X X X		X X X X X X X X

4 most   next 8 bits   8 least significant
significant bits   bits

It is useful to regard these words as digits, not of radix 10, but of radix 2^8 or 256. Thus, if the three words in a number are X, Y and Z (moving from left to right), the value of the number is $X.256^2 + Y.256^1 + Z.256^0$.

This analogy helps to explain the method used for addition and subtraction of these long numbers. It is done in stages, one 'digit' at a time, starting with the least significant, and with a carry being transferred between stages if necessary. The carry is generated automatically at each stage of the addition, and is remembered in C; it can be used in the next stage of addition by the ADC instruction.

Suppose it is required to add a three-word number (P, Q, R) to another one (X, Y, Z). The code would be:

```
LDA A,  Z    ↑ ADD LEAST SIGNIFICANT WORDS
ADA A,  R
STA A,  Z    ↑ STORE LEAST SIGNIFICANT PART OF
             ↑ RESULT
LDA A,  Y    ↑ ADD NEXT PAIR OF WORDS
ADC A,  Q    ↑ USING CARRY FROM PREVIOUS STAGE
STA A,  Y    ↑ STORE NEXT PART OF RESULT
LDA A,  X    ↑ ADD MOST SIGNIFICANT WORDS
ADC A,  P    ↑ USING CARRY FROM PREVIOUS CARRY
STA A,  X    ↑ STORE MOST SIGNIFICANT PART OF RESULT
```

The reader should look up the precise definitions of the instructions used in Table 6.3. He will note that LDA and STA conveniently leave C unchanged.

This description has assumed that the long numbers are unsigned — that is, zero or positive. The system works equally well with signed numbers in two's complement form, provided that the sign bit is replicated in the most significant word. A signed 20-bit number would be represented as follows:

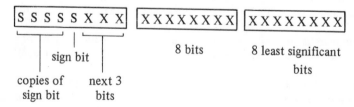

Direct mode

One of the most obvious aims of the design of the 6800 microprocessor was to save store space by making instructions as compact as possible. Normally, instructions that refer to cells in the store occupy three words and have 16-bit addresses; they are said to be in *extended* mode.

Some store reference instructions – specifically those in Table 6.3 but *not* those in Table 6.4 – have a special form called the 'direct' mode. An address in the direct mode is only eight bits long, and gives an instruction size of two words (instead of three). An eight-bit address is limited to the range 0–255, and any cell referred to by a 'direct' instruction must lie in this restricted area of store.

As well as being shorter than their 'extended' counterparts, direct instructions are faster by one clock pulse.

The programmer should know of the existence of the direct mode, but need not trouble to use it explicitly, since the assembler will automatically use the direct mode whenever it can. All that is necessary is to ensure that the items referred to are in the first 256 words of the store. The modes assigned by the assembler are illustrated below:

```
. = 100
MA:    0        ↑ ALLOCATED TO CELL 100
MB:    0        ↑ ALLOCATED TO CELL 101
. = 400
PA:    0        ↑ ALLOCATED TO CELL 400
...
LDA  A, MA      ↑ DIRECT MODE (BECAUSE MA < 256)
STA  A, PA      ↑ EXTENDED MODE (BECAUSE PA ⩾ 256)
CLR  MB         ↑ EXTENDED MODE (BECAUSE CLR HAS NO
                ↑ DIRECT MODE FORM)
```

Arrays

Tables and lists are among the most common types of data structure in computing. Examples include truth tables, lists of coefficients for interpolation in numerical control, and tables of sample values derived from a continuous analogue signal source.

The essential difference between a table and a group of separately named variables is that the values in the table form a family. Sometimes it may be necessary to access them all one after the other, or it may be required to choose one whose position cannot be determined in advance, but depends on the current value of some other variable.

The main mechanisms for array manipulation in the 6800 are the *index register* and the *index mode*.

The index register is a 16-bit register in the CPU. In general, it holds the address of a location in the store. A few special instructions are provided to manipulate its contents, as detailed below.

Addressless instructions on the index register

These instructions are listed in Table 7.1. The increment and decrement instructions set Z if the result is zero, and clear it otherwise. The other indicators are not affected.

The instructions in this group occupy one byte and take four clock pulses to be executed.

Table 7.1

Mnemonic	Result in				Explanation
	N	Z	V	C	
DEX	.	↕	.	.	Decrement index register by 1.
INX	.	↕	.	.	Increment index register by 1.
TXS	.	.	.	.	Copy index register to stack pointer and subtract 1.
TSX	.	.	.	.	Copy stack pointer to index register and add 1.

Index register operations with operands

Each of these instructions (Table 7.2) uses a 16-bit operand (or address). All the operations on the index register are done in 16-bit (double-length) arithmetic, and the indicators are set accordingly.

Table 7.2

Mnemonic	Result in				Explanation
	N	Z	V	C	
LDX	↕	↕	R	.	Load index register with operand.
STX	↕	↕	R	.	Store index register in stated address.
CPX	↕	↕	↕	.	Compare index register with operand.

The instructions in this group can take various modes, including:

- *Extended mode.* The instruction format is:

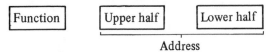

The operand, being two words long, is taken from the cell addressed and the one with the next highest address. Index register instructions in extended mode take five cycles to execute, except STX, which takes six cycles.

- *Direct mode.* This assumes that the operand is in the first 256 words of store, and only one word of address is needed. The instruction format is:

and the execution time is four (or five) cycles. The operand itself is, of course, still 16 bits long.

- *Immediate mode.* An instruction in the immediate mode contains its own operand:

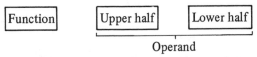

and takes three cycles. The immediate mode is not available for STX.

Index mode

Like the extended mode, the index mode applies to nearly every instruction except branches and those that need no addresses. The format of an instruction in index mode is:

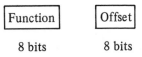

In the written form, the offset is preceded by the symbol X and enclosed in brackets.

When an instruction in index mode is executed the effective address is the result of adding the offset and the (current) value of the index register. For example:

```
LDX  #100        ↑ SETS INDEX REGISTER = 100
LDA  A, X(50)    ↑ LOADS ACC A WITH CONTENTS OF
                 ↑ CELL 150 BECAUSE (100 + 50) = 150
ADA  A, X(51)    ↑ ADDS CONTENTS OF CELL 151 to ACC A
                 ↑ BECAUSE (100 + 51) = 151
INX              ↑ ADDS 1 TO INDEX REGISTER, GIVING 101
ADA  A, X(51)    ↑ ADDS CONTENTS OF CELL 152 TO ACC A
                 ↑ BECAUSE (101 + 51) = 152
```

In general, an instruction in index mode takes one cycle longer than its counterpart in extended mode.

Accessing an array

First, we shall consider a method of accessing all the elements of an array, one after the other, in regular order. This can be done as follows:

1. Load the address of the last element of the array into the index register.
2. Refer to an element of the array by using an indexed instruction with offset = 0.
3. Decrement the index register by 1.
4. Compare the index register with the address of the first element of the array. If its value is greater or equal, return to step 2. Otherwise stop.

The key to this sequence is that step 2 is carried out repeatedly, for each value of the index register between the address of the last element and that of the first. For example, consider an array of ten cells defined as follows:

```
ARRAY:  0    ↑ TEN CELLS. ADDRESS OF FIRST IS ARRAY
. = .+8      ↑ AND ADDRESS OF LAST IS
ARRAYTOP: 0  ↑ ARRAY TOP
```

To add up the contents of all ten we put:

```
        CLR A              ↑ CLEAR A
STEP1:  LDX #ARRAYTOP      ↑ SET UP INDEX REGISTER
STEP2:  ADD A, X(0)        ↑ ADD NEXT ELEMENT OF
                           ↑ ARRAY TO A
STEP3:  DEX                ↑ DECREMENT INDEX REGISTER
STEP4:  CPX #ARRAY         ↑ TEST FOR LAST VALUE
        BPL  STEP 2        ↑ BACK IF LOOP NOT COMPLETED
```

A more realistic example is offered by a security system which has to monitor 50 signals, each of which is connected to the system through an A/D converter, and has a danger value, in digital terms, of 100 units or over. We suppose that the A/D converters are interfaced at addresses ?FF00 to ?FF31, and the routine which takes action if it finds anything wrong starts at the instruction labelled HELP:

```
LOOPA:    LDX #?FF31
LOOPB:    LDA A, X(0)
          CMP A, #100
          BPL HELP
          DEX
          CPX #?FF00
          BPL LOOPB
          BRA LOOPA
```

This program has two nested loops, the inner one to interrogate each signal and the outer one to repeat the scanning process continually until a critical signal is found.

The reader should verify that, with a 500 kHz clock, this program is certain to detect any value in the 'danger zone' within 2.2 ms.

The second method of access is used to select a particular element for an array assuming that its position in the array is not known in advance but is the result of calculation. The method relies on calculating the address of the element by adding the (known) address of the array and the required position. Double-length arithmetic must be used since addresses are 16-bit quantities, but there is no instruction for 16-bit addition in the index register. The code to do the task assumes that the position of the required element is in accumulator B, and that two adjacent workspace cells labelled WA and WB are available.

```
    LDX #BASE       ↑ LOAD ADDRESS OF FIRST ELEMENT
                    ↑ TO INDEX REG
    STX WA          ↑ STORE TOP HALF IN WA, BOTTOM
                    ↑ HALF IN WB
    ADA B, WB       ↑ ADD POSITION TO BOTTOM HALF
    STA B, WB       ↑ OF BASE ADDRESS
    BCC WX          ↑ TEST CARRY
    INC WA          ↑ INCREMENT TOP HALF IF NECES-
                    ↑ SARY
WX: LDX WA
    LDA A, X(0)     ↑ LOAD SELECTED ELEMENT
```

In any program that makes use of this method of array access, it is often wise to group these instructions into a subroutine, so that it can be called from any point in the program. The definition of such a subroutine might be:

> SUBROUTINE AA: entered with the base address of an array (i.e. the address of the first element) in the index register, and the relative position of a selected element in accumulator B; the subroutine calculates the absolute address of the selected element and delivers it in the index register.

As a final illustration we shall discuss the problem of generating a two-digit decimal display. The definition of such a subroutine has already been given on page 72. The program assumes that two seven-segment displays are connected to the address bus at location ?F100

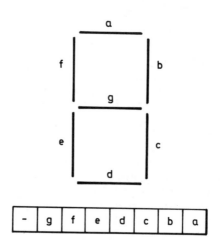

Figure 7.2

and ?F101. Each display is driven by a latch, which clocks in the data on the system bus when its address is selected. The segments are arranged as shown in *Figure 7.2*, and light up when *zeros* are present in the latch. The bit-patterns for producing the ten decimal digits (and −) are shown in *Figure 7.3*.

Suppose that the binary patterns for the digits are stored in an array, in the order 0–9. To display a digit *n*, all that is necessary is to select the *n*th member of the array and send it to a seven-segment display.

The full code for the subroutine can now be given. It is not a complete program in itself, but would be included as a 'component' of some other, larger program.

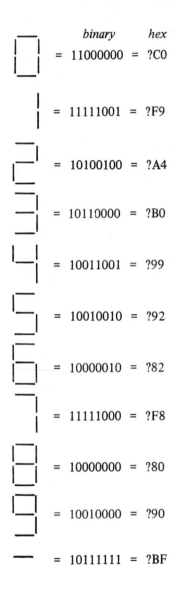

	binary	*hex*
=	11000000	= ?C0
=	11111001	= ?F9
=	10100100	= ?A4
=	10110000	= ?B0
=	10011001	= ?99
=	10010010	= ?92
=	10000010	= ?82
=	11111000	= ?F8
=	10000000	= ?80
=	10010000	= ?90
=	10111111	= ?BF

Figure 7.3

```
↑  SUBROUTINE FOR DECIMAL DISPLAY
TENS:=       ?F100        ↑  DEFINE PERIPHERAL ADDRESSES
UNITS:=      ?F101
DIGITS:      ?C0, ?F9,    ↑  SHAPES TO BE DISPLAYED
             ?A4, ?B0,    ↑  ASSEMBLED IN CONSECUTIVE
             ?99, ?92,    ↑  CELLS STARTING AT 'DIGITS'
             ?82, ?F8, ?80,
             ?90
DISPLAY:     TST A        ↑  TEST RANGE OF A
             BMI FAULT
             CMP A, #100
             BPL FAULT    ↑  JUMP IF < 0 OR ≥ 100
             LDA B,#?FF   ↑  SET B = −1
DIA:         INC B        ↑  COUNT NO OF TENS
             SUB A,# ̶10   ↑  IN A. RESULT IN B
             BPL DIA      ↑  B ENDS WITH TENS DIGIT
             ADD A,#10    ↑  RESTORE A ≥ 0. A IS UNITS DIGIT
             LDX #DIGITS↑ CALCULATE  ADDRESS  OF  TENS
             BSR ARAC     ↑  DIGIT BY SUBROUTINE
             LDA B, X(0)
             STA B, TENS  ↑  DISPLAY SHAPE OF TENS DIGIT
             LDX #DIGITS
             TAB          ↑  COPY UNITS DIGIT TO B
             BSR ARAC     ↑  CALCULATE  ADDRESS  OF  UNITS
                          ↑  DIGIT
             LDA B, X(0)  ↑  DISPLAY SHAPE OF UNITS DIGIT
             STA B, UNITS
             RTS          ↑  RETURN TO CALLING PROGRAM
FAULT:       LDA A, #?BF  ↑  FAULT. DISPLAY−
             STA A, TENS
             STA A, UNITS
             RTS          ↑  RETURN TO CALLING PROGRAM
ARAC:        STX ARA      ↑  SUBROUTINE FOR ADDRESS CAL-
                          ↑  CULATION
             ADA B, ARB
             STA B, ARB
             BCC ARC
             INC ARA
ARC:         LDX ARA
             RTS          ↑  RETURN TO CALLING PROGRAM
ARA:         0            ↑  WORKSPACE
ARB:         0
```

The chapter closes on a final point. Many of our sample programs have shown tables, workspace cells and instructions all in nearby cells. This is satisfactory if the program is to be used in RAM, but if it is to be implanted in ROM then any location that is changed (such as workspace or the stack) should be kept separate and placed in the part of the address space to contain RAM. This will be illustrated in later programs.

8

Control of peripheral devices (1)

The control of most peripheral devices is a complex matter. So far, this fact has been concealed by a very careful choice of peripherals, but in this chapter the real problems of the area will be faced and illustrated by a realistic practical example.

In previous chapters, all the devices chosen for discussion were instantaneous in their response. Thus the setting of a switch could be sensed at any time, and an LED display could absorb any data sent to it at electronic speed.

In practice, most peripherals take finite times to react to any signal from a microcomputer. There are two reasons:

- Some devices rely on mechanical motion. This category includes magnetic tapes, cassettes, magnetic disks, tape readers, numerically controlled machine tools, and any other device with a solenoid or motor.
- Some peripherals are used to transmit and receive data over lines of limited bandwidth, like GPO telephone lines.

The management of slow devices is difficult because the system cannot simply read or write information at any time, but must wait until the device is ready for a further exchange. With some devices, like a disk rotating at a steady speed or a remote transmitter not under the control of the local system, the information must be exchanged within a certain time of the device becoming ready, otherwise it is lost. This is called the *crisis time* of the device.

Direct control

Most devices can exchange 'status' information as well as data. Thus a device can present the computer with a 'ready/busy' bit to indicate

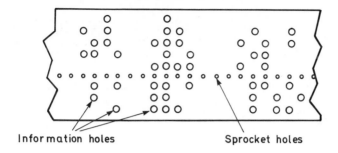

Information holes   Sprocket holes

Figure 8.1

whether it is ready for an exchange of data, and it may also have other bits to show whether it is switched on, or whether there is a fault condition of some kind. Going in the other direction, the system can send control signals to the device to make it start and stop as necessary.

To give an approximate but realistic illustration of these points consider a reader for eight-hole paper tape, as shown in *Figure 8.1*. Each frame on the tape has eight hole positions for data, and one sprocket hole, which is always punched and is smaller than the data holes. The data in a frame is called a 'character', and is often (but not necessarily) the representation of a character in ASCII code.

In the reader, the tape is passed between a light and a row of nine photocells, each of which can 'see' one of the hole positions. The signals from the eight data positions are valid whenever the tape is centred on a frame. This condition can be checked by the presence of the sprocket hole.

The tape is moved from frame to frame by a stepping motor. A single positive pulse a few microseconds long makes it start and move the tape one frame. The movement takes several milliseconds, and any further pulses applied while the tape is still in motion are simply ignored.

Figure 8.2 shows how the reader might be interfaced to the microcomputer.

E000 is for reading the data on each frame, and is connected to the outputs of the data photocells.

E001 is for sensing the position of the tape, and is connected to the sprocket hole photocell (SHP).

E002 is for motor control (MC).

The broad strategy for reading a new character assumes that the character over the photocells has already been read, and uses the following steps:

Address   Layout

E000

DP$_7$	DP$_6$	DP$_5$	DP$_4$	DP$_3$	DP$_2$	DP$_1$	DP$_0$

E001

							SHP

E002

							MC

Figure 8.2

1. Start the motor.
2. Wait for the next frame to appear.
3. Read the character which is then visible.

Once the motor has been started, its motion appears to the microcomputer to be of geological slowness, taking thousands of machine cycles before the next frame comes into view. Step 2 must therefore be split into two sections:

2(a)   Wait until the present sprocket hole disappears.
2(b)   Then wait until the next one appears.

A subroutine to read a single character and deliver it in accumulator A might take the following form:

```
DATA: = ?E000            ↑   DEFINE INTERFACE
                         ↑   ADDRESSES

SPROCKET:= ?E001
MOTOR:= ?E002

CHARIN:  CLR MOTOR       ↑   SUBROUTINE STARTS
         LDA A, #1       ↑   SEND A +VE PULSE
         STA A, MOTOR    ↑   TO START MOTOR
         CLR MOTOR
CHA:     LDA A, SPROCKET ↑   WAIT FOR SPROCKET TO
                         ↑   VANISH
         BNE CHA         ↑   (JUMP BACK IF STILL
                         ↑   VISIBLE)
CHB:     LDA A, SPROCKET ↑   WAIT FOR NEXT SPROCKET
                         ↑   TO APPEAR
         BEQ CHB         ↑   JUMP BACK IF NOT VISIBLE
         LDA A, DATA     ↑   READ NEXT CHARACTER
         RTS             ↑   EXIT
```

Control by polling

One feature of the control method described in the previous section is that the entire system is obliged to wait, doing nothing useful, while the tape is being moved on to the next character. This is perfectly reasonable if there is nothing else to be done, but in some circumstances it is unacceptable. For example, the microprocessor may be responsible for several devices all running at the same time, as in a message-switching exchange or a five-axis numerically controlled machine tool. If a system spent all its attention on one device, it would mean ignoring the others.

The most satisfactory way of dealing with this problem is by *polling*. This consists of making the processor examine the statuses (ready/busy bits) of all the devices, one after the other, in cyclic fashion. As soon as a device is found that is ready for another transfer, a suitable exchange is made and the scanning is resumed.

To illustrate this idea we take another practical example: an exchange for interactive terminals. It will be necessary to lead up to this system by two intermediate programs.

A terminal is a device used for communication with a computer. It can take various forms including airline booking terminals, visual displays for computer-assisted instruction, or terminals for information retrieval. A terminal incorporates two independent devices — a keyboard and a display unit (which may be a typewriter, a matrix printer or a cathode-ray tube). There is no direct connection between them; any text to be typed is only displayed because it is sent to the remote computer from the keyboard and then sent back to the display.

The speed at which data can be handled by a display is limited, either by the mechanics of the printer or by the bandwidth of the connecting line. In this example, we shall assume a speed of ten characters per second.

Terminals are interfaced to microprocessors through special controller chips called UARTs (Universal Asynchronous Receiver Transmitters). The keyboard and the display each use two words of interface: one for the data, and one for the status of the device. The layout for the display is this:

First word:

Data (character to be displayed)	

Second word:

Status	R/B

When the display is ready for another character, the ready/busy bit in the status word indicates a 1. As soon as a new character is written to the data word transmission starts automatically (this is one of the functions of the UART) and the ready/busy bit returns to 0. After 0.1

second, when transmission is complete, the ready/busy bit changes back to a 1, showing that another character can be accepted.

The keyboard interface layout is similar, but the data transfer is in the other direction. The ready/busy bit stays at 0 ('busy') until a key on the keyboard has been pressed and the data transmitted. Then the new character is presented at the data word, and the status changes to 'ready'. When the data word is read by the system, the UART switches the status back to 'busy' so that another character can be read.

Terminals have one useful property: the speed of typing on the keyboard cannot exceed the speed at which the display can absorb characters. If a microcomputer is used to 'pump' characters from a keyboard to the associated display, the only limiting factor to the overall speed is the keyboard.

Here, then, is a program that 'echoes back' the text typed on a terminal keyboard by sending it to the associated display.

```
TITLE "TERMINAL ECHO PROGRAM"
DD:= ?F800          ↑  DISPLAY DATA INTERFACE
                    ↑  ADDRESS
DS:= ?F801          ↑  DISPLAY STATUS INTERFACE
                    ↑  ADDRESS
KD:= ?F802          ↑  KEYBOARD DATA INTERFACE
                    ↑  ADDRESS
KS:= ?F803          ↑  KEYBOARD STATUS INTERFACE
                    ↑  ADDRESS
BEGIN: LDA A, KS    ↑  EXAMINE KEYBOARD STATUS
       BEQ BEGIN    ↑  WAIT UNTIL READY
       LDA A, KD    ↑  CHARACTER READY. READ IT TO
                    ↑  ACC A
                    ↑  THIS CLEARS THE WAY FOR A
                    ↑  NEW CHARACTER
       STA A, DD    ↑  SEND IT TO THE DISPLAY. THIS
                    ↑  STARTS TRANSMISSION. THE
                    ↑  DISPLAY IS ASSUMED READY,
                    ↑  BECAUSE IT IS (IN GENERAL)
                    ↑  FASTER THAN THE KEYBOARD
       BRA BEGIN
START BEGIN
```

This program will be expanded to handle ten terminals. It is assumed that the first terminal is interfaced at F800 to F803, the second at F804 to F807, the third at F808 to F80B, and the last at F824 to F827. The program uses the *index* mode to work its way down the interface words. Thus the value in the index register is F800 when the first terminal is being serviced, F804 when it is the turn of the second one, and so on.

TITLE "ECHO PROGRAM FOR 10 TERMINALS"

```
FIRST:= ?F800              ↑ ADDRESS OF FIRST TERMINAL
                           ↑ INTERFACE GROUP
LAST:= ?F824               ↑ ADDRESS OF LAST TERMINAL
                           ↑ INTERFACE GROUP

BEGIN: LDX #FIRST          ↑ LOAD ADDRESS OF FIRST INTER-
                           ↑ FACE
BEA:   LDA A, X(3)         ↑ LOOK AT KEYBOARD STATUS OF
                           ↑ NEXT TERMINAL
       BEQ BEB             ↑ JUMP IF NOT READY
       LDA A, X(2)         ↑ CHARACTER READY. MOVE IT TO
                           ↑ PRINTER
       STA A, X(0)
BEB:   CPX # LAST          ↑ TEST IF LAST TERMINAL
                           ↑ EXAMINED
       BEQ BEGIN           ↑ START AGAIN AT BEGINNING IF SO
       INX                 ↑ OTHERWISE ADD 4 TO
       INX                 ↑ INDEX REGISTER
       INX
       INX
       BRA BEA             ↑ RE-ENTER LOOP
START BEGIN
```

When a terminal is being serviced, the system cannot control the speed of the typist; on the other hand, every character must be properly handled. This means that a keyboard is a device with a crisis time. In our example, with a transmission rate of 10 characters per second, it is 100 ms.

In the program given above, the time needed for one cycle of the inner loop, with a transfer of data, is 52 cycles or 104 μs. In the worst case, assuming that every device had delivered a character, the time for the whole loop would be 10×104 μs = 1.04 ms. This, then, is the guaranteed maximum interval between successive examination of each keyboard. Since the crisis time is 100 ms, the system is 'safe'. The maximum number of devices that could be serviced by a similar program would be $100/0.104 = 961$. On the other hand, if each terminal ran at 400 characters per second, the maximum number would now be only 24.

A practical example

The reader has now covered sufficient groundwork to consider the teletype exchange, which is the main example in this chapter. The design
of such an exchange is a realistic practical problem, and the reader, who
has so far looked only at very simple programs, must expect a sudden
increase in the level of complexity. There are, however, very few new
ideas to be mastered; the difference is that for the first time several
ideas are used in combination. The two keys to mastering the program
are:

- to understand the way that data is used;
- to approach the program in the same way as it is written; that is,
  hierarchically.

The teletype exchange is to link twenty teletypes to five lines connected to a remote computer, as shown in *Figure 8.3*. All lines run at
ten characters per second, and each computer line behaves in exactly
the same way as a teletype.

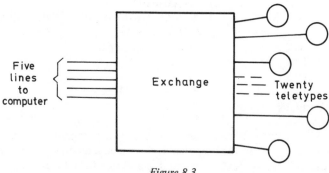

Figure 8.3

As far as possible, the exchange is to be invisible to the user; the aim
is for it to give the illusion that each teletype is permanently connected
to the computer. This is in practice impossible, because there are more
teletypes than there are lines, but the following specification is not far
from the ideal.

When the owner of a terminal wants to use the computer, he types
any character except 'bell'. If the exchange can find a free line to the
computer, it allocates it to the terminal and then maintains the connection by handling all the data traffic in either direction. If there are no

free lines the exchange sends a 'bell' character back to the user's terminal. This character makes the terminal sound a distinctive note, and tells the user that all lines to the computer are currently busy. When the dialogue with the computer is finished the user frees the line by typing the bell character. The line can then be allocated to a different terminal.

The first stage in planning such a system is to decide on the layout of the interface words and other essential items of data. We assume:

- twenty terminal lines with interface blocks of four words each, starting at F100;
- five computer lines with interface blocks of four words each, starting at F200.

Each interface block is arranged in the order:

Transmitter data }
Transmitter status } Information to display or computer

Receiver data }
Receiver status } Information from keyboard or computer

At any moment, some terminals are connected to particular computer lines, and other terminals and lines are free. In an electromechanical exchange the state of each terminal and computer line would be represented by the position of a uniselector, but the microcomputer exchange uses a data structure to record the same information.

The terminals are numbered 0 to 19, and the computer lines 0 to 4. The information about connections is kept in two arrays:

TR has twenty elements, numbered 0 to 19, one for each terminal;
LR has five elements, numbered 0 to 4, one for each line.

Suppose that terminal 17 is connected to line 2; then element 17 of TR contains a 2, and element 2 of LR contains a 17.

If a terminal or line is not in use, its state is recorded by a −1. To give an example, consider the following:

TR:

−1	3	−1	−1	−1	−1	0	−1	−1	−1
−1	−1	−1	−1	−1	−1	−1	2	−1	−1

LR:

6	−1	17	1	−1

This shows that terminal 1 is connected to line 3,
    terminal 6 is connected to line 0,
    terminal 17 is connected to line 2.

If terminal 12 should request a line, it would be allocated line 1, and the arrays would change to

TR:

−1	3	−1	−1	−1	−1	0	−1	−1	−1
−1	−1	1	−1	−1	−1	−1	2	−1	−1

LR:

6	12	17	1	−1

This method of storage is redundant because if one of the arrays is known, the other can be worked out from it; but it offers the advantage that if a character is received from any source, its destination can be looked up immediately.

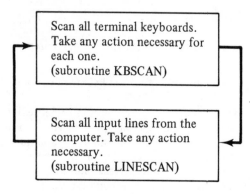

Figure 8.4

At the uppermost level, the exchange program works in two phases, which follow each other cyclically: see *Figure 8.4*. The two phases are each made into subroutines, so that the main program (at the highest level) will be:

```
BEGIN:      LDS #STACKTOP    ↑ SET STACK POINTER
            LDX #LR+4        ↑ CLEAR TR AND LR TO −1
            LDA A, #?FF      ↑ SET A = −1
ML:         STA A, X(0)      ↑ STORE IN ELEMENT OF TR
                             ↑ OR LR
            DEX
            CPX #TR          ↑ TEST
            BNE ML           ↑ JUMP BACK
MAINLOOP:   JSR KBSCAN       ↑ CALL KBSCAN
            JSR LINESCAN     ↑ CALL LINESCAN
            BRA MAINLOOP     ↑ RETURN TO MAINLOOP
```

Routine KBSCAN is simply required to check the twenty terminals in sequence. At this level, the elementary action is that of checking and servicing a single terminal. This can be made into a subroutine called TSERVE, so that all KSBCAN needs to do is to call TSERVE twenty times, once for each terminal device. Whenever TSERVE is called, the number of the terminal concerned is passed over in accumulator A. The code for KBSCAN is:

```
KBSCAN:  CLR A          ↑ SET ACC A = 0
KBA:     STA A, KBB     ↑ PRESERVE ACC A (IN
                        ↑ CASE TSERVE SPOILS IT)
         JSR TSERVE     ↑ CALL TSERVE
         LDA A, KBB     ↑ RESTORE ACC A
         INC A          ↑ INCREMENT
         CMP A, #20     ↑ LOOP ROUND
         BNE KBA
         RTS            ↑ RETURN TO MAIN PROGRAM
         0              ↑ WORKSPACE
KBB:     0
```

The discussion now moves to TSERVE, the routine called to inspect an incoming terminal line and take action if necessary. The line number is given in accumulator A.

The action to be taken when a keyboard character is received depends on two things:

- Is a line already allocated to this terminal?
- Is the character typed a bell?

There are four combinations of circumstances, and the required action for each one is as follows:

NN (Line not allocated, character not bell): Look for a free line. If found, make the allocation by altering the terminal and line records appropriately, and then send the received character to the computer down the newly allocated line. If all the lines are engaged, return a 'bell' to the originating terminal.

NY (Line not allocated, character is bell). Do nothing. (This rule is made in order to guarantee that a 'bell' character will always leave the terminal disconnected.)

YN (Line allocated, character not bell). Send character to computer on allocated line.

YY (Line allocated, character is bell). De-allocate line by altering terminal and line records. Return 'bell' to originating terminal.

TSERVE needs to gain access to elements of arrays such as TR or the array of interface words. The program must therefore include an array access subroutine. This routine is called AA, and is entered with the base address of an array in the index register, and the offset of a wanted element in accumulator B. The actual address of the element is returned in the index register.

```
AA:     STX AAB        ↑ ACCESS ARRAY ELEMENT
        ADD B, AAC
        STA B, AAC     ↑ ADD B TO (AAB, AAC)
        BCC AAD
        INC AAB
AAD:    LDX AAB        ↑ LOAD RESULT
        RTS
AAB:    0
AAC:    0
```

TSERVE inspects the status register of the appropriate terminal, and takes any action necessary. This may involve calling one of subroutines NN, YN or YY, as appropriate. Whenever one of these subroutines is called, the terminal number is passed over in accumulator A, and the character just read from the terminal in accumulator B.

```
TSERVE: TAB            ↑ COPY A TO B
        ASL B          ↑ QUADRUPLE B (EACH TERMINAL
        ASL B          ↑ HAS 4 INTERFACE WORDS)
        LDX #?F100
        JSR AA         ↑ GET ADDRESS OF INTERFACE
                       ↑ BLOCK
        LDA B, X(3)    ↑ GET STATUS WORD
        BEQ TSE        ↑ EXIT (NO ACTION IF CHAR NOT
                       ↑ READY)
TSA:    LDA B, X(2)    ↑ GET CHAR AND STORE
        STA B, TSB     ↑ TEMPORARILY
        TAB            ↑ GET ENTRY FROM
        LDX # TR       ↑ CONNECTION TABLE TR
        JSR AA
        LDA B, X(0)
        BMI TSC        ↑ JUMP IF NO LINE ALLOCATED
        LDA B, TSB     ↑ GET CHARACTER
        CMP B, #BELL   ↑ TEST IF BELL
        BNE TSD        ↑ JUMP IF NOT
        JSR YY         ↑ IS BELL (AND LINE ALLOCATED)
        RTS            ↑ CALL YY, AND THEN RETURN
TSD:    JSR YN         ↑ IS NOT BELL (LINE IS ALLO-
                       ↑ CATED)
        RTS            ↑ CALL YN (AND THEN RETURN)
```

```
TSC:      LDA B, TSB      ↑ LINE NOT ALLOCATED
          CMP B, #BELL    ↑ GET CHARACTER
          BEQ TSE         ↑ SKIP IF BELL
          JSR NN          ↑ ELSE CALL NN
TSE:      RTS
TSB:      0
```

The next part of the design task is to write the subroutines YY, YN and NN.

YY is invoked to de-allocate a line from a terminal. It must locate the appropriate entries in both tables TR and LR, and replace them by −1. The entry in TR can be reached by direct access, using the base address of TR and the (known) terminal number in A. The entry in LR can be found by searching for an entry equal to A.

```
YY:       LDX #LR         ↑ PREPARE TO SEARCH LR
YYB:      CMP A, X(0)     ↑ JUMP WHEN VALUE FOUND
          BEQ YYA
          INX             ↑ ELSE INCREMENT X AND JUMP
                          ↑ BACK
          BRA YYB         ↑ TEST NOT NECESSARY IF DATA
                          ↑ STRUCTURE CORRECT
YYA:      LDA B, #?FF     ↑ PLANT −1 IN LR
          STA B, X(0)
          TAB             ↑ GET ADDRESS OF ENTRY IN
          LDX #TR         ↑ TR
          JSR AA
          LDA B, #?FF
          STA B, X(0)     ↑ PLANT −1 IN TR
          RTS             ↑ EXIT
```

Routine YN has the job of sending the characters down the line allocated to the current terminal. It must first look up the identity of this line in table TR, and then work out the address of the corresponding interface block. Two calls to AA are necessary.

```
YN:       STA B, YNA      ↑ STORE CHARACTER
                          ↑ TEMPORARILY
          TAB
          LDX #TR
          JSR AA
          LDA B, X(0)     ↑ GET CORRESPONDING LINE
                          ↑ NUMBER FROM TR
          LDX #?F200
          ASL B
          ASL B
```

```
          JSR AA              ↑ GET ADDRESS OF INTERFACE
                             ↑ BLOCK
          LDA B, YNA
          STA B, X(0)         ↑ SEND CHARACTER
          RTS
YNA:      0
```

The last and perhaps most complex subroutine is NN, the one that attempts to allocate a line to a terminal. It begins by searching the array LR for an entry of −1, which indicates an unused line. If it fails to find one, it sends a 'bell' character back to the terminal which issued the request. Otherwise it makes suitable entries in both LR and TR, and then sends the received character over the line, using subroutine YN which is convenient for the purpose.

```
NN:       STA A, NNA          ↑ DUMP A TEMPORARILY
          STA B, NNB          ↑ DUMP RECEIVED CHARACTER
          CLR A               ↑ SET LINE TO BE INSPECTED IN
                             ↑ A, STARTING AT 0
NND:      TAB
          LDX #LR
          JSR AA
          LDA B, X(0)         ↑ GET ENTRY FOR THIS LINE
          BMI NNC             ↑ JUMP IF −1 FOUND
          INC A               ↑ ADVANCE A. SEE IF END
          CMP A, #5           ↑ OF LR REACHED
          BNE NND             ↑ JUMP BACK IF NOT
          LDA B, NNA          ↑ FREE LINE NOT FOUND. SEND
                             ↑ BELL
          ASL B               ↑ GET 4 TERMINAL NO IN B
          ASL B
          LDX #?F100
          JSR AA              ↑ GET ADDRESS OF TERMINAL
                             ↑ BLOCK
          LDA B, #BELL
          STA B, X(0)
          RTS                 ↑ OUT
NNC:      LDA B, NNA          ↑ FREE LINE FOUND. ITS NO IS
                             ↑ IN A
          STA B, X(0)         ↑ ENTER TERM NO IN LR
          LDA B, NNA          ↑ GET ADDRESS OF ELEMENT IN
                             ↑ TR
          LDX #TR
          JSR AA
```

```
        STA A, X(0)        ↑ STORE LINE NUMBER THERE
        LDA B, NNB         ↑ NOW SEND CHARACTER
        LDA A, NNA
        JSR YN
        RTS
```

The complete hierarchy descended from KBSCAN has now been examined. The subroutines descended from LINESCAN are basically similar, but they are much simpler because when a character is received from a computer line there are only two possibilities:

- If the line is allocated to a terminal, pass the character on to that terminal.
- If the line is not allocated, do nothing.

The actual code for these routines is given below:

```
↑ LINESCAN CALLS LSERVE FOR EACH COMPUTER LINE

LINESCAN: CLR A             ↑ SET ACC A = 0
LBA:      STA A, LBB        ↑ PRESERVE ACC A
          JSR LSERVE        ↑ CALL LSERVE
          LDA A, LBB        ↑ RESTORE ACC A
          INC A             ↑ INCREMENT
          CMP A, #5         ↑ LOOP AROUND
          BNE LBA
          RTS               ↑ RETURN
LBB:      0                 ↑ WORKSPACE
↑ LSERVE SERVICES THE COMPUTER LINE WHOSE NUMBER IS
↑ GIVEN IN ACCUMULATOR A
LSERVE:   TAB               ↑ LOOK AT INTERFACE BLOCK
          ASL B
          ASL B
          LDX #?F200
          JSR AA
          LDA B, X(3)       ↑ GET RECEIVER STATUS
          BEQ LSE           ↑ JUMP IF NO CHAR RECEIVED
          LDA B, X(2)       ↑ GET CHAR AND STORE
          STA B, LSB
          TAB               ↑ SEE IF LINE ALLOCATED
          LDX #LR
          JSR AA
          LDA B, X(0)
          BMI LSE           ↑ JUMP IF NOT
          LDX #?F100        ↑ ELSE GET ADDRESS OF TER-
                            ↑ MINAL INTERFACE BLOCK
```

```
        ASL B
        ASL B
        JSR AA
        LDA B, LSB        ↑ SEND CHARACTER
        STA B, X(0)
LSE:    RTS
```

The whole program has now been designed. Its hierarchic structure is shown in *Figure 8.5*,

where (A)———▶(B) means 'A calls B'.

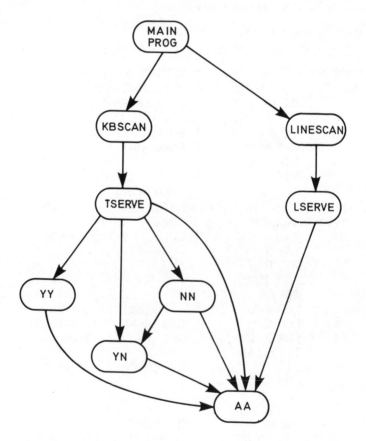

Figure 8.5

The entire program in its assembled version appears in *Figure 8.6*. The stack, arrays, and workspace variables have been put at the beginning of the address space so that they can be referred to by instructions in the 'direct' mode. The code has been placed at location ?200, where it resides in a ROM. The assembler shows that 128 words of RAM and 512 words of ROM are sufficient to support the system.

An important question to be settled at this point is whether the system can in fact handle the load it is designed for. Now the worst conceivable combination of events is as follows:

Initially, all terminals are quiescent, and none is allocated a line. Suddenly all of them, simultaneously, make requests for connection. The system should allocate lines to the first five and then refuse connection to the others, returning a bell character to each one. Calculations show that all twenty requests will be serviced in about 25.3 ms. This figure can be arrived at as follows:

Time for AA	62 μs	
Time for YN (including calls to AA)	232 μs	
Time for NN (assuming fifth line found free)	1038 μs	
Time for NN (assuming rejection)	768 μs	
Time for TSERVE (assuming NN is called and finds fifth line free)	1316 μs	
Time for TSERVE (assuming NN is called, but fails to make a connection)	1056 μs	
Time for KBSCAN (assuming that TSERVE is called, five new connections are made and 15 requests rejected)	23.4 ms	(1)
Time for LSERVE, assuming a character is received	346 μs	
Time for LINESCAN, assuming five characters are received	1.9 ms	(2)

Total time in worst case: (1) + (2) = 25.3 ms.

The crisis time of a single terminal is 100 ms, so the system is 'safe'; indeed it would support almost four times as many lines and terminals before running into danger of collapsing.

If the same system were to be used with faster terminals (say with a 10 ms crisis time) its correct operation could not be guaranteed. The designer would have several options:

1. To use a faster processor.
2. To 'polish' the program (an analysis would show that the system spends most of its time executing routine AA, and if calls to this routine could be reduced by using a more complex data structure the program would run somewhat faster).

SYMBOL	HEX	DEC	OCT
BELL	7	7	7
TR	0	0	0
LR	15	21	25
KBB	1B	27	33
AAB	1D	29	35
AAC	1F	31	37
TSB	21	33	41
YNA	23	35	43
NNA	25	37	45
NNB	27	39	47
LBB	29	41	51
LSB	2B	43	53
STACK	2D	45	55
STACKTOP	5F	95	137
BEGIN	2000	8192	20000
ML	2008	8200	20010
MAINLOOP	2010	8208	20020
KBSCAN	2018	8216	20030
LINESCAN	20D4	8404	20324
KBA	2019	8217	20031
TSERVE	2034	8244	20064
AA	2026	8230	20046
AAD	2031	8241	20061
TSE	2067	8295	20147
TSA	2041	8257	20101
TSC	205E	8286	20136
TSD	205A	8282	20132
YY	2068	8296	20150
YN	2082	8322	20202
NN	209A	8346	20232
YYB	206B	8299	20153
YYA	2072	8306	20162
NND	209F	8351	20237
NNC	20BE	8382	20276
LBA	20D5	8405	20325
LSERVE	20E2	8418	20342
LSE	210A	8458	20412

```
                          1
                          2
                          3  TITLE "TELETYPE EXCHANGE PROGRAM"
                          4
                          5  BELL:=7              =ASCII CODE FOR THE BELL CHARACTE
                          6  .=0
   0    0    0            7  TR: 0
                          8  .=.+19              =SPACE FOR ARRAY TR
  15    0    0            9  LR: 0
                         10  .=.+4               =SPACE FOR ARRAY LR
  1B    0    0           11  KBB: 0              =WORKSPACE FOR KBSCAN
  1D    0    0           12  AAB: 0              =WORKSPACE FOR AA
  1F    0    0           13  AAC: 0
  21    0    0           14  TSB: 0              =WORKSPACE FOR TSERVE
  23    0    0           15  YNA: 0              =WORKSPACE FOR YN
  25    0    0           16  NNA: 0              =WORKSPACE FOR NN
  27    0    0           17  NNB: 0
  29    0    0           18  LBB: 0              =WORKSPACE FOR LINESCAN
  2B    0    0           19  LSB: 0              =WORKSPACE FOR LSERVE
  2D    0    0           20  STACK: 0            =LOWER END OF STACK
                         21  .=.+48
  5F    0    0           22  STACKTOP: 0         =UPPER END OF STACK
                         23
                         24
```

Figure 8.6(a)

```
                25
                26 * HERE BEGINS CODE SECTION
                27 * FIRST, THE CODE FOR THE MAIN PROGRAM
                28 * LOCATED AT ADDRESS 2000 (HEX)
                29
                30 .=?2000
                31
2000 8E   0 5F  32 BEGIN:      LDS  #STACKTOP    *SET STACK POINTER
                33
2003 CE   0 19  34              LDX  #LR+4        *CLEAR TR AND LR TO -1
2006 86 FF      35              LDA  A,#?FF       *SET A=-1
2008 A7  0      36 ML:          STA  A,X(0)       *STORE IN ELEMENT OF TR OR LR
200A 9          37              DEX
200B 8C  0  0   38              CPX  #TR          *TEST IF LOOP COMPLETE
200E 26 F8      39              BNE  ML           *JUMP BACK IF NOT
                40
2010 BD 20 18   41 MAINLOOP:JSR KBSCAN            *CALL KBSCAN
2013 BD 20 D4   42              JSR  LINESCAN     *CALL LINESCAN
2016 20 F8      43              BRA  MAINLOOP     *RETURN TO MAINLOOP
                44
                45 * SUBROUTINE KBSCAN CALLS TSERVE FOR EACH OF 20
                46 * TERMINAL LINES
                47
2018 4F         48 KBSCAN:     CLR  A            *SET ACC A =0
2019 97 1B      49 KBA:        STA  A,KBB        *PRESERVE ACC A
201B BD 20 34   50              JSR  TSERVE       *CALL TSERVE
201F 96 1B      51              LDA  A,KBB        *RESTORE ACC A
2020 4C         52              INC  A            *INCREMENT IT
2021 81 14      53              CMP  A, #20       *LOOP ROUND
2023 26 F4      54              BNE  KBA
2025 39         55              RTS               *RETURN TO MAIN PROGRAM
                56
                57 * SUBROUTINE AA HELPS WITH ARRAY ACCESS
                58 * BY ADDING THE CONTENTS OF ACC. B TO
                59 * THE INDEX REGISTER.
                60
2026 DF 1D      61 AA:         STX  AAB          *STORE BASE ADDRESS IN AAB,AAC
2028 DB 1F      62              ADD  B,AAC
202A D7 1F      63              STA  B,AAC        *ADD ACC. B TO (AAB,AAC)
202C 24  3      64              BCC  AAD
202E 7C  0 1D   65'             INC  AAB          *INCREMENT MS. HALF
2031 DF 1D      66 AAD:        LDX  AAB          *LOAD RESULT
2033 39         67              RTS
                68
                69
                70
                71
                72 * ROUTINE TSERVE SERVICES EACH TERMINAL LINE.
                73 * IF A CHARACTER HAS BEEN RECEIVED IT TAKES
                74 * APPROPRIATE ACTION
                75
2034 16         76 TSERVE:     TAB               *COPY A TO B
2035 58         77              ASL  B            *QUADRUPLE B (EACH TERMINAL
2036 58         78              ASL  B            *HAS 4 INTERFACE WORDS)
2037 CE F1  0   79              LDX  #?F100
203A BD 20 26   80              JSR  AA           *GET ADDRESS OF INTERFACE BLOCK
203D E6  3      81              LDA  B, X(3)      *GET STATUS WORD
203F 27 26      82              BEQ  TSE          *EXIT IF CHAR NOT READY
2041 E6  2      83 TSA:        LDA  B,X(2)       *GET CHAR AND STORE
2043 D7 21      34              STA  B, TSB       *TEMPORARILY
2045 16         85              TAB               *GET ENTRY FROM CONNECTION
2046 CE  0  0   86              LDX  #TR          *TABLE TR
2049 BD 20 26   87              JSR  AA
204C E6  0      88              LDA  B, X(0)
```

Figure 8.6(b)

```
204E 2B  E    89           BMI  TSC      *JUMP IF NO LINE ALLOCATED
2050 D6 21    90           LDA  B, TSB   *GET CHARACTER
2052 C1  7    91           CMP  B, #BELL *TEST IF BEEL
2054 26  4    92           BNE  TSD      *JUMP IF NOT
2056 BD 20 68 93           JSR  YY       *IS BELL (AND LINE ALLOCATED
2059 39       94           RTS           *CALL YY TO DE-ALLOCATE
              95                         *AND THEN RETURN
205A BD 20 82 96  TSD:     JSR  YN       *IS NOT BELL (A LINE ALLOCAT
205D 39       97           RTS           *CALL YN (AND THEN RETURN)
205E D6 21    98  TSC:     LDA  B,TSB    *LINE NOT ALLOCATED, GET
2060 C1  7    99           CMP  B,#BELL  *CHARACTER, AND TEST IF BELL
2062 27  3    100          BEQ  TSE      *OUT IF SO
2064 BD 20 9A 101          JSR  NN       *ELSE CALL NN
2067 39       102 TSE:     RTS           *RETURN TO CALLING PROGRAM
              103
              104
              105 * SUBROUTINE YY DE-ALLOCATES A LINE FROM THE
              106 * TERMINAL WHOSE NUMBER IS IN ACC. A
              107
              108
2068 CE  0 15 109 YY:      LDX  #LR      *PREPARE TO SEARCH LR
206B A1  0    110 YYB:     CMP  A, X(0)  *JUMP WHEN VALUE FOUND
206D 27  3    111          BEQ  YYA
206F  8       112          INX           *ELSE INCREMENT X AND JUMP B
2070 20 F9    113          BRA  YYB
2072 C6 FF    114 YYA:     LDA  B, #?FF  *PLANT -1 IN LR
2074 E7  0    115          STA  B, X(0)
2076 16       116          TAB           *GET ADDRESS OF ENTRY IN TR
2077 CF  0  0 117          LDX  #TR
207A BD 20 26 118          JSR  AA
207D C6 FF    119          LDA  B, #?FF
207F E7  0    120          STA  B, X(0)  *PLANT (-1)
2081 39       121          RTS           *EXIT
              122
              123
              124
              125 *SUBROUTINE YN SENDS THE CHARACTER IN B DOWN THE LIN
              126 *ALLOCATED TO THE TERMINAL WHOSE NUMBER IS IN A
              127
              128
2082 D7 23    129 YN:      STA  B, YNA   *STORE CHARACTER TEMPORARILY
2084 16       130          TAB
2085 CE  0  0 131          LDX  #TR
2088 BD 20 26 132          JSR  AA
208B E6  0    133          LDA  B, X(0)  *GET CORRECT LINE NUMBER FRO
208D CE F2  0 134          LDX  #?F200
2090 58       135          ASL  B
2091 58       136          ASL  B
2092 BD 20 26 137          JSR  AA       *GET ADDRESS OF INTERFACE BL
2095 D6 23    138          LDA  B, YNA   *RESTORE ORIGINAL CHARACTER
2097 E7  0    139          STA  B, X(0)  *SEND CHARACTER
2099 39       140          RTS           *RETURN
              141
              142
              143 * SUBROUTINE NN ATTEMPTS TO ALLOCATE A LINE
              144 * TO A TERMINAL SPECIFIED IN A
              145
209A 97 25    146 NN:      STA  A, NNA   *DUMP A TEMPORARILY
209C D7 27    147          STA  B,NNB    *DUMP RECEIVED CHARACTER
209E 4F       148          CLR  A        *SET LINE TO BE INSPECTED IN
209F 16       149 NND:     TAB
20A0 CE  0 15 150          LDX  #LR
20A3 BD 20 26 151          JSR  AA
```

Figure 8.6(c)

```
20A6 E6   0      152            LDA B, X(0)      *GET ENTRY FOR THIS LINE
20A8 2B 14       153            BMI NNC          *JUMP IF =1 FOUND
20AA 4C          154            INC A            *ADVANCE A, SEE IF END
20AB 81   5      155            CMP A, #5        * OF LR REACHED
20AD 26 F0       156            BNF NND          *JUMP RACK IF NOT
20AF D6 25       157            LDA B, NNA       *FRFE LINE NOT FOUND, SEND BELL
20B1 58          158            ASL B            *GFT 4 TIMES TERMINAL NO. IN B
20B2 58          159            ASL B
20B3 CE F1  0 160              LDX #?F100
20B6 BD 20 26 161              JSR AA           *GET ADDRESS OF TERMINAL BLOCK
20B9 C6   7      162            LDA B, #BELL
20BB E7   0      163            STA B, X(0)
20BD 39          164            RTS              *OUT
                 165
20BE D6 25       166 NNC:       LDA B, NNA       *LINE FOUND, ITS NUMNER IS IN A
20C0 E7   0      167            STA B, X(0)      *ENTER TFRM NO IN LR
20C2 D6 25       168            LDA B, NNA       *GET ADDRESS OF FLEMENT IN TR
20C4 CE   0  0 169             LDX #TR
20C7 BD 20 26 170              JSR AA
20CA A7   0      171            STA A, X(0)      *STORF LINE NUMBER THERE
20CC D6 27       172            LDA B, NNB       *NOW SFND CHARACTER
20CE 96 25       173            LDA A, NNA
20D0 BD 20 82 174              JSR YN
20D3 39          175            RTS
                 176
                 177
                 178
                 179 *LINESCAN CALLS LSFRVE FOR FACH COMPUTER LINF
20D4 4F          180 LINESCAN: CLR A
20D5 97 29       181 LBA:       STA A, LBB       *PRESFRVF ACC A
20D7 BD 20 E2 182              JSR LSERVE       *CALL LSERVE
20DA 96 29       183            LDA A, LBB       *RESTORE ACC A
20DC 4C          184            INC A
20DD 81   5      185            CMP A, #5        *INCREMENT,TEST AND LOOP ROUND
20DF 26 F4       186            BNE LBA
20E1 39          187            RTS              *RETURN
                 188
                 189 *LSERVE SERVICFS THE COMPUTER LINE WHOSE NUMBER
                 190 * IS IN ACCUMULATOR A
20E2 16          191 LSERVE:    TAB              *LOOK AT INTERFACE BLOCK
20E3 58          192            ASL B
20E4 58          193            ASL B
20E5 CE F2  0 194              LDX #?F200
20E8 BD 20 26 195              JSR AA
20EB E6   3      196            LDA B, X(3)      *GET RECEIVER STATUS
20ED 27 1B       197            BEQ LSE          *JUMP IF NO CHAR RECEIVED
20EF E6   2      198            LDA B, X(2)      *GET CHAR AND STORE
20F1 D7 2B       199            STA B, LSB
20F3 16          200            TAB              *SEE IF LINE ALLOCATED
20F4 CE   0 15 201             LDX #LR
20F7 BD 20 26 202              JSR AA
20FA E6   0      203            LDA B, X(0)
20FC 2B   C      204            BMI LSE          *JUMP IF NOT
20FE CE F1  0 205              LDX #?F100        *ELSE GET ADDRESS OF
2101 58          206            ASL B            *TERMINAL INTERFACE BLOCK
2102 58          207            ASL B
2103 BD 20 26 208              JSR AA
2106 D6 2B       209            LDA B, LSB       *SEND CHARACTFR
2108 E7   0      210            STA B, X(0)
210A 39          211 LSE:       RTS              *RETURN
                 212 START BEGIN
    0 FAULTS AND    0 WARNINGS
```

Figure 8.6(d)

3. To change the specification of the system so that, for example, a
   lack of immediate response to a request for a line should not be
   counted as a 'failure'.
4. To take a risk; the worst case described may seem rather unlikely to
   arise in practice.

The correct choice would depend on the circumstances, but options 2
and 4 are not recommended. 'Optimisation' of a working program is an
excellent way of introducing errors. Jackson's rules of optimisation
state:

1. Don't.
2. If you must, don't do it now.

As for taking risks with programs, most good designers consider that
their equipment is already sufficiently at risk from power failures, component breakdowns and sabotage. Further risks, which could be avoided,
are hardly ever justified.

9

Control of peripheral devices (2)

Polling, the method of peripheral control described in Chapter 8, is suitable for systems where the peripheral devices all have similar characteristics of data rates and crisis times. Sometimes the load is unbalanced; one or two devices may have a much higher speed and a much shorter crisis time than the rest. For example, a plant control system that normally polls round 500 observation points, taking a leisurely cycle time of several seconds, may need to respond to an 'alarm' input within 10 milliseconds. If the alarm is merely placed in the polling loop, and interrogated in its turn, the response time clearly cannot be guaranteed.

Plural polling

One simple way of ensuring a fast response is to include the critical peripheral in the polling loop several times over. Consider a system with twelve slow devices S1 to S12, and one fast device F. The maximum service time for each device is 1 millisecond. The slow devices have a crisis time of 100 ms, but the fast device must be serviced within 4 ms of making a request. The polling loop shown in *Figure 9.1* would be adequate.

A typical 'worst case' arises when S1, S2 and S3 are all in need of service, and F generates a request when S1 is about to be polled. F is still (just) serviced within 4 milliseconds.

This approach can be used right up to the point where the fast device occupies every second position in the loop. The essential relation is that the service time of the fast device, *plus* the service time of any other device, must together be less than the crisis time of the fast device. If this relation cannot be satisfied, the method of interrupts must be used.

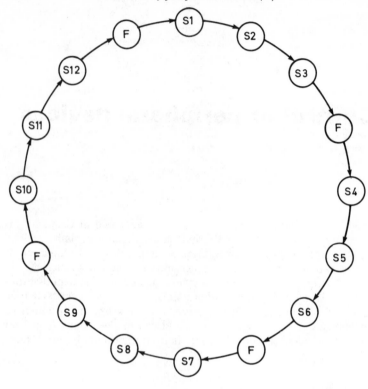

Figure 9.1

Interrupts

Interrupts are frustrating, difficult and dangerous, and their use should be avoided wherever possible.

Interrupts were devised in order to let a system, busy on a task of low priority, handle a short high-priority job without delay. The normal running of the machine is interrupted while the special job is done, after which normal work is resumed.

The program that executes the special job is called an 'interrupt routine'. It is in many ways like a subroutine; for example, when an interrupt routine is running the details of the main program are stored on the stack. In other ways it is quite different: it is not invoked by the main program but by an event in a peripheral device, and it is not necessarily in communication with the main program at all.

The mechanism for calling interrupt routines varies widely on different microprocessor systems. On the 6800 interrupts are called as follows.

There is an input line to the CPU called $\overline{\text{IRQ}}$. This stands for (not) Interrupt ReQuest. The line is connected to V_{cc} through a resistor and is normally high. Whenever a device needs to attract the attention of the CPU, it pulls the $\overline{\text{IRQ}}$ line down with an open-collector gate.

The CPU's response, if any, takes place when it has finished the current instruction (instructions are never interrupted part-way through). The CPU has an indicator called I, which is the interrupt mask. If the mask is set high, the interrupt request is ignored and the program proceeds in its normal sequence. If, however, the mask is clear, an interrupt actually takes place. First, all the indicators and the contents of all the CPU registers except the stack pointer are copied out to the stack for preservation, and the stack pointer is advanced accordingly. Next, the CPU fetches an address from locations FFF8 and FFF9, and loads it in to the program counter. Then the interrupt mask is set high. Lastly, the system begins to execute the program at the address read from FFF8 and FFF9, which is the beginning of the interrupt routine.

While the interrupt routine is running, no more interrupts can be accepted on the $\overline{\text{IRQ}}$ line, because the interrupt mask has been set.

When the interrupt routine ends, it executes an RTI instruction. This is similar to RTS, and returns control to the program that was originally interrupted, after restoring all the indicators and CPU registers from the stack.

A program can be interrupted between any two instructions, and the mechanism described here allows the program to be resumed without any 'awareness' that the interrupt has occurred. In practice this is only true if the interrupt routine does not alter any of the store registers used by the main program, or any of the stack cells used to preserve the CPU contents. If this condition is violated the main program will give different results, or fail in different ways, on successive trials. This is because interrupts can occur at any time, and each one may corrupt the main program in a different way.

Notwithstanding these difficulties, a simple example follows. A system with a slow scanning cycle must respond immediately to an

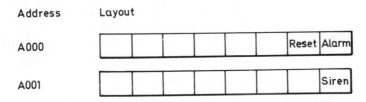

Figure 9.2

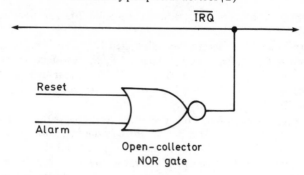

Figure 9.3

alarm by sounding a siren. The siren must continue until a 'reset' button is pressed, and the alarm is no longer on.

The inputs and the siren are arranged as shown in *Figure 9.2*. The two input lines can both generate interrupts, by the connection shown in *Figure 9.3*.

The code for the interrupt routine is given below. It is arbitrarily placed at address 1000 (decimal).

```
↑  ALARM MANAGEMENT
          . = 1000
          LDA A, ?A000        ↑  GET INPUTS
          BIT A, #1           ↑  SEE IF ALARM SET
          BNE LXX             ↑  JUMP IF NOT
          LDA A, #1
          STA A, ?A001        ↑  START SIREN
          RTI                 ↑  RETURN TO SCANNING
LXX:      CMP A, #2           ↑  TEST IF 'RESET' ON BY ITSELF
          BNE LXY             ↑  JUMP IF NOT
          CLR ?A001           ↑  STOP SIREN
LXY:      RTI
          . = FFF8            ↑  THIS IS THE ADDRESS OF THE
                              ↑  INTERRUPT ROUTINE IN FFF8,
                              ↑  FFF9. "FDB" INTRODUCES
          FDB 1000            ↑  A DOUBLE-LENGTH CONSTANT
```

This example is artificially simple in that the alarm management has no connection whatever with the main scanning program. In general, interrupt routines interact with 'main' programs in subtle ways.

Many systems have two or more peripherals that need to be serviced by interrupts. These devices will usually all be connected to the IRQ line, and an interrupt can be generated by any one of them. The interrupt routine must then begin by polling all the interrupt-causing devices to discover which one actually produced the interrupt.

Often two or more devices will require service at the same time. When the first device is serviced, the IRQ line will still be held low by the other devices. The effect is that an RTI instruction simply returns control to the beginning of the interrupt routine, and the polling starts again.

Suppose the interrupting devices are called $1, 2, 3 \ldots n$ in the order of increasing crisis times. The actual crisis times are $C_1, C_2, C_3 \ldots C_n$, and the service times are $S_1, S_2, S_3 \ldots S_n$. The longest service time is S_{max}.

In the worst case, all devices come up with a service request at the moment that the device with the longest service time has just begun to be serviced. As the devices are polled in the order $1, 2, 3 \ldots n$, the following relations can be written down to guarantee service within the crisis time:

For device 1: $C_1 > S_{max} + S_1$
For device 2: $C_2 > S_{max} + S_1 + S_2$

For device j: $C_j > S_{max} + \sum_{k=1}^{j} S_k$

Where timing is really critical, the polling procedure can be speeded up by using a priority encoder chip as a special input device.

The 6800 chip has another, non-maskable interrupt line called $\overline{NMI}$. A signal on this line will interrupt anything, even an interrupt routine. It is normally used only for events of overriding importance, like imminent power failures. The interrupt routine address for $\overline{NMI}$ is kept in FFFC and FFFD.

Systems that depend on interrupts can only be declared 'safe' if very complex and binding rules are followed. The difficulties of using interrupts effectively are so great that at least one manufacturer of computer systems designed for extreme reliability has done away with interrupts as a method for controlling peripheral devices. The X250, made by Plessey, uses only polling to manage its peripherals.

General-purpose interface controllers

Microprocessors are used to control many different types of device. Each needs its own specific design of interface. Some of the more simple

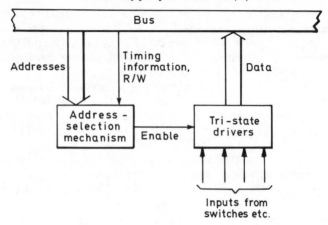

Figure 9.4

types of parallel interface are shown in *Figures 9.4 to 9.7*. They have one important common feature: the transfer of information between the bus and the device takes place only when:

- the address on the address lines is the one assigned to the device;
- the read/write line from the processors is set appropriately;
- the timing signals (i.e. the clock and a VMA line which is asserted when the address is valid) are in the correct state.

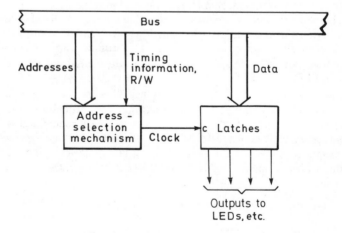

Figure 9.5

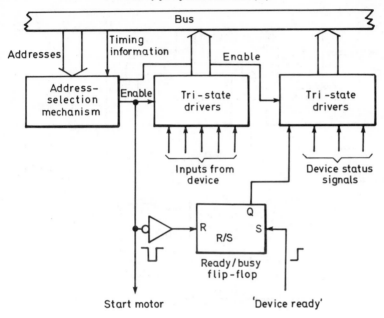

Figure 9.6

In the diagrams, all the input signals to the bus are generated by tristate drivers, enabled by the address and timing selection mechanism. Similarly, output signals are fed to latches, for which the strobe pulses are again generated by the address and timing selection mechanism.

Figures 9.4 and 9.5 show 'instantaneous' (time-independent) input and output, which would be suitable for switches, LEDs, and so on.

Figures 9.6 and 9.7 show typical interfaces for time-dependent devices, such as paper-tape readers or punches. As explained in Chapter 8, each device needs two interface words: one for the data and one for status information (ready/busy, serviceable or not, and so on).

The interface maintains a flip-flop that indicates the ready/busy status of the device. The entire status word can be sensed at any time by reading at the appropriate address. When the data word is read or written (as appropriate), the enable or clock pulse is used to set the ready/busy flip-flop to 'busy', and also to start the motor in the device. As soon as the device is ready for another data transfer it sends a positive edge, which switches the ready/busy flip-flop back to 'ready'.

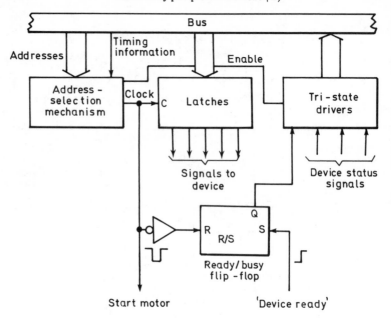

Figure 9.7

In *Figure 9.8*, a time-dependent input device is shown equipped with an interrupt capability. If necessary, the interrupt can be generated whenever the device becomes ready. This makes the system read the next character of data and restart the device as soon as possible.

The interrupt facility must be switchable, for otherwise whenever the device was not in use, it would generate a constant interrupt signal and prevent the system from working properly. There is therefore a *third* interface word, which consists of a one-bit latch to enable the interrupt. When this latch contains a 1, the 'ready' signal is allowed to pull down the IRQ line through an open-collector NAND gate. If the latch is set to zero, the interrupt is inhibited.

Suppliers of microprocessors are in a highly competitive field. One way to gain an advantage is to provide a system that, for a given capability, uses fewer separate components than that of the opposition. Many manufacturers therefore provide 'general-purpose interface chips', which provide most of the interface functions in a convenient way.

In the manufacture of LSI circuits, there is a strong financial incentive to have long production runs of the same component. On the other hand, there is little penalty for complexity. In consequence, most

115

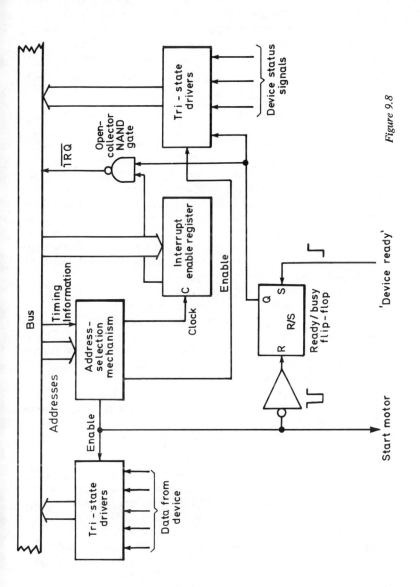

Figure 9.8

makers do not attempt to produce a different interface chip for every type of application, but market only one or two 'general-purpose' types, which are highly adaptable. This flexibility makes the circuits seems complicated, and the documentation, if read 'in the abstract', is often difficult to understand. However, if the reader has a specific problem in mind, these difficulties form much less of a barrier than might be expected.

The 6820 general-purpose interface controller

Motorola's 6820 can be used to control all parallel interfaces. It takes over data latching, data buffering, status recording, interrupt management, timing control, and all the functions of any parallel interface except for address selection and signal conditioning.

Internally, the 6820 is divided into two almost identical halves called A and B. They are not independent, because they share a common control and data path to the bus, but it is nevertheless reasonable to describe only one half. It can be assumed that the other half is the same unless the contrary is said. Where necessary, the suffixes A and B are used to distinguish components belonging to the two halves.

The 6820 occupies four consecutive words in the address space. The first two belong to half A, and the second to half B.

Figure 9.9 shows a 6820 in its normal configuration. The diagram assumes that the four interface words are located at EFFC to EFFF (a choice that minimises the number of invertors needed in the address selection mechanism). The 6820 is selected whenever one of these four addresses appears as a valid address on the bus.

Input RSI distinguishes between half A (RSI = 0) and half B (RSI = 1). It is shown connected to a_1, ensuring that the A interface words are at EFFC and EFFD, the lower two of the four addresses.

Although it has only two addresses, each half of the 6820 actually has *three* interface words:

- A *control register* called CRA (or CRB). The six bottom bits of this register can be loaded by program, and the whole register can also be read back. Its contents control the behaviour of the half-chip, and are generally set up, once and for all, at the beginning of a program. The control register of each half is selected when RSO = 1. In the example, the addresses of CRA and CRB are EFFD and EFFF respectively. The layout of the control register is shown in *Figure 9.10*; the meaning of the fields is explained below.
- A *data direction register* called DDR. This register holds eight binary

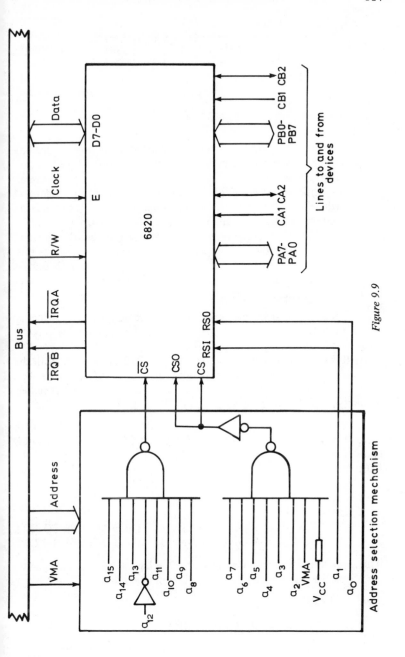

Figure 9.9

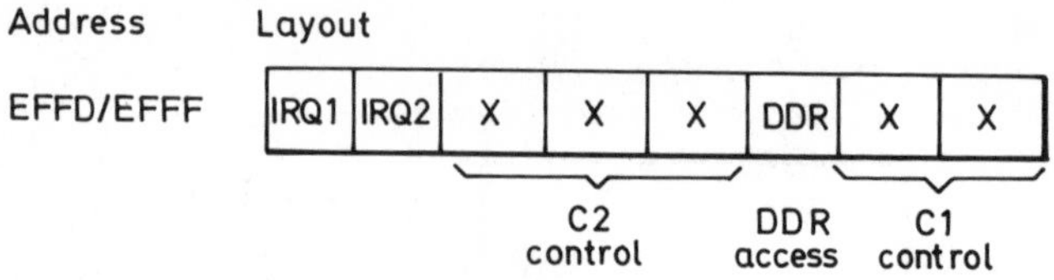

Address   Layout

EFFD/EFFF | IRQ1 | IRQ2 | X | X | X | DDR | X | X |

C2 control   DDR access   C1 control

Figure 9.10

digits. It may be written to, but there is seldom any point in reading its contents, as they cannot be changed by anything except a program instruction.

● A *data buffer* called DB. This is used for input or output of data on the eight lines P0 to P7. The action of each bit of DB depends on the contents of the corresponding bit of DDR. If a stage of DDR contains a 0, the corresponding line is treated as an input, and when DB is read by a program, the corresponding signal is sent to the bus. If the stage of DDR holds a 1, the line becomes an output. Data is held in a latch, and the data bus is strobed for new data whenever the system writes to the DB.

The DDR and DB share the *same* address. The distinction is made by bit 2, the 'DDR access' field in the control register. A 0 here selects the DDR, and a 1 indicates the data buffer.

At this stage it can be shown how a single 6820 can provide both the time-independent interfaces shown in *Figures 9.4 and 9.5*. Half A is used for input, and lines PA0 to PA7 are connected to the switches. Similarly, half B is used for output, and PB0 to PB7 drive the LEDs.

```
CLR  ?EFFD          ↑ CLEAR CR(A): GIVES ACCESS TO DDR A
CLR  ?EFFF          ↑ CLEAR CR(B): GIVES ACCESS TO DDR B
CLR  ?EFFC          ↑ SET DDR(A) = 0 (I.E. ALL INPUTS)
LDA A, #?FF
STA A, ?EFFE        ↑ SET DDR(B) = 11111111 (I.E. ALL OUT-
                    ↑ PUTS)
LDA A, #4
STA A, ?EFFD        ↑ SET CR(A) = 4: GIVES ACCESS TO DBA
STA A, ?EFFF        ↑ SET CR(B) = 4: GIVES ACCESS TO DBB
```

When this initial programming sequence has been executed, data can be read from the input buffer by an instruction like:

LDA A, ?EFFC

and it can be written to the output buffer by:

STA A, ?EFFE

just as if specially built interface drivers, latches and address-selection mechanisms were present.

The data direction can be set independently for each bit of the word. This makes it possible for input and output devices with only a small number of lines to share the same address. Care is needed in writing software to take account only of those bits which are actually significant, as any current outputs will be fed back as inputs as well. Suppose four heat detectors and four alarm bells are configured as follows:

EFFC: | HD#1 | HD#2 | HD#3 | HD#4 | AL#1 | AL#2 | AL#3 | AL#4 |

The sequence to initialise the 6820 would be:

```
CLR   ?EFFD          ↑ CLEAR CR(A)
LDA   A, #?F         ↑ SET DDR(A) = 00001111
STA   A, ?EFFC
LDA   A, #4
STA   A, ?EFFD       ↑ SET CR(A) = 4
```

Thereafter, to test the heat detectors, irrespective of the state of the alarm bells, one could write:

```
LDA   A, ?EFFC       ↑ GET DATA BUFFER
AND   A, #?F0        ↑ MASK WITH 11110000
BNE   HELP           ↑ JUMP IF ANY DETECTOR SET
```

For time-dependent devices, each half of the 6820 provides two ready/busy flip-flops, and two control lines. The flip-flops are called IRQ1 and IRQ2, and are located at bits 7 and 6 of the control register, so that their states can be read by the CPU.

IRQ1 and IRQ2 are both capable of producing interrupts when they change from 'busy' to 'ready'. The action of reading the *data buffer* in a half of the 6820 (not the control register) has the side-effect of returning both IRQ1 and IRQ2 in that half to 0, or 'busy'.

Each half has two special control lines C1 and C2. C1 can only be used as an input from the device being controlled, whereas C2 is bidirectional.

Normally, C1 carries ready/busy information from the device, and serves to set up the IRQ1 flip-flop. The precise method depends on the setting of the C1 control field in CR. If bit 1 of CR = 0, IRQ1 is set 'ready' by a negative edge on C1; if bit 1 of CR = 1, IRQ1 is set 'ready' by a positive edge. The system is therefore adaptable to either polarity of signal. Bit 0 of CR serves to enable the interrupt facility. If this bit is set to 1 when IRQ1 is switched to ready, an interrupt occurs.

Table 9.1

CR1	CR0	Effect
0	0	IRQ1 set on negative edge of C1. Interrupt disabled.
0	1	IRQ1 set on negative edge of C1. Interrupt enabled.
1	0	IRQ1 set on positive edge of C1. Interrupt disabled.
1	1	IRQ1 set on positive edge of C1. Interrupt enabled.

The control of C1, which is identical on both sides of the 6820, can be summarised by Table 9.1.

The behaviour of C2 is determined by bits 5, 4 and 3 of CR. If bit 5 is a 0, C2 (and IRQ2, to which it is linked) behaves in exactly the same way as C1 and IRQ1. This is set out in Table 9.2.

When bit 5 of CR = 1, C2 becomes an output. It can be used flexibly to supply start pulses of various types to the device being controlled.

When bits 5 and 4 of CR are both 1, C2 follows the value of bit 3 of CR. By sending a suitable sequence of values to CR, a pulse train of any characteristics whatever can be generated on C2.

Table 9.2

CR5	CR4	CR3	Effect
0	0	0	IRQ2 set on negative edge of C2. Interrupt disabled.
0	0	1	IRQ2 set on negative edge of C2. Interrupt enabled.
0	1	0	IRQ2 set on positive edge of C2. Interrupt disabled.
0	1	1	IRQ2 set on positive edge of C2. Interrupt enabled.

Table 9.3

CR5	CR4	CR3	Half (A/B)	Effect on C2 (CA2 or C)
1	0	0	A	Negative pulse in CA2 starts after a 'read' operation on DBA. Ends when IRQA1 is set ready.
1	0	0	B	Negative pulse on CB2 starts after a 'write' operation on DBB. Ends when IRQB1 is set ready.
1	0	1	A	Negative pulse in CA2 starts after a 'read' operation in DBA, and lasts for one clock period.
1	0	1	B	Negative pulse on CB2 starts after a 'write' operation in DBB, and lasts for one clock period.
1	1	X	A	CA2 follows CRA3.
1	1	X	B	CB2 follows CRB3.

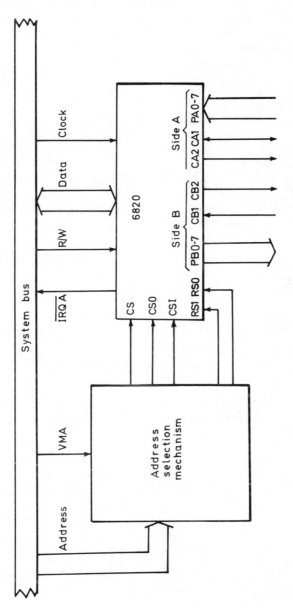

Figure 9.11

When bit 4 of CR is clear, C2 is made to carry negative pulses. The event that starts the pulse is *different* in the two halves of the 6820. On side A, it is a 'read' operation from the data buffer; on side B, it is a 'write' operation to the data buffer.

The event that ends the pulse is selected by bit 3 of CR. If CR3 = 0, then the pulse ends as soon as IRQ1 is set ready. If CR3 = 1, the timing is derived from the system clock, and will normally produce a pulse one machine cycle wide.

The action is again summarised in Table 9.3.

To give a final illustration, it will be shown how one 6820 chip can serve to interface both the output device shown in *Figure 9.7* and the interrupting input device in *Figure 9.8*.

The general arrangement is shown in *Figure 9.11*. The input device is driven by side A, and the output by side B. In both cases C2 is used to supply a short 'start' pulse to the device motor, and C1 returns the 'ready' signal. The initial configuring sequence, which assumes the devices addresses used earlier, would be as follows:

```
CLR  ?EFFD        ↑ CLEAR CR(A) AND CR(B)
CLR  ?EFFF
CLR  ?EFFC        ↑ SET DDRA FOR INPUT
LDA  A, #?FF
STA  A, ?EFFE     ↑ SET DDRB FOR OUTPUT
LDA  A, #?2F      ↑ CONFIGURE CRA: CA2 CONTROL = 101
STA  A, ?EFFD     ↑ CA1 CONTROL = 11
LDA  A, #?2E      ↑ CONFIGURE CRB: CB2 CONTROL = 101
STA  A, ?EFFF     ↑ CB1 CONTROL = 10
```

In normal use, each device must be tested to ensure it is ready before information is exchanged. To output a character in accumulator B the code would now be:

```
XX:  TST  ?EFFF     ↑ TEST CRB
     BPL  XX        ↑ JUMP BACK IF IRQ1 = 0
     LDA  A, ?EFFE  ↑ READ DBB TO CLEAR IRQ1
     STA  B, ?EFFE  ↑ WRITE  CHARACTER. BECAUSE  CB2
                    ↑ CONTROL = 101, THIS AUTOMATICALLY
                    ↑ SENDS A SHORT PULSE TO THE DEVICE
                    ↑ MOTOR
```

If an interrupt is received (but not necessarily for the input device attached to side A), part of the interrupt routine to be executed should be:

```
LDA A, ?EFFD   ↑ LOOK AT CRA
BPL  YY        ↑ JUMP IF NOT READY
LDA A, ?EFFC   ↑ READ DBA. THIS AUTOMATICALLY
               ↑ SENDS A PULSE ON CA2 TO THE
               ↑ DEVICE MOTOR, BECAUSE CA2 CON-
               ↑ TROL = 101.
               ↑ IT ALSO CLEARS IRQ1
STA  A, DUMP   ↑ STORE NEW CHARACTER
RTI            ↑ EXIT FROM INTERRUPT ROUTINE
YY:
```

The 6850 asynchronous communication interface adaptor

This unit can be used whenever asynchronous transmission of data is needed. Its function is broadly similar to that of the 6820, but considerably simpler, so the study of its details is left as an exercise to the reader.

10

Comparing microprocessors

Since the first microprocessor was introduced, the number of different types has grown rapidly, and is now (1978) over 200. Furthermore, another new design is announced frequently. Clearly a detailed taxonomy of all the systems available would not only occupy several volumes, but would be out of date before it was printed. This chapter, therefore, begins with a single illustrative comparison between the Motorola 6800 and the Intel 8080. It then goes on to consider some of the variable aspects of microprocessors in a more general way, and to suggest features that are relevant to particular fields of application.

The Intel 8080

The 8080 is in many ways similar to the 6800. It too has an eight-bit word, an address space of 2^{16}, and programmable interface chips. However, the internal arrangement of the CPU is somewhat different. The layout is shown in *Figure 10.1*.

As with the 6800, the accumulator is the centre of operations. The three indicators N, Z and C are also similar to their 6800 counterparts, but instead of V, the P indicator shows the *parity* of the most recent result.

Two other registers in the CPU are the stack pointer and the program counter. Their uses are again very like those of their 6800 counterparts, although all addresses in the 8080 are given as absolute 16-bit quantities. The 8080's branch instructions, of which it has a full set, are all therefore three words long.

The CPU also contains six more eight-bit registers, labelled B, C, D, E, H and L. They can be used individually or in pairs (B, C), (D, E) and H, L) as 16-bit registers. The contents of (H, L) are often interpreted as a memory address.

Most of the one-word instructions of the machine include one or

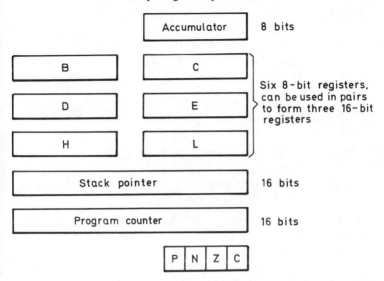

Figure 10.1

two three-bit fields to specify a register or memory cell. The code used is:

000	B
001	C
010	D
011	E
100	H
101	L
110	the memory cell addressed by (H, L)
111	A

For example, the 'MOV' instruction has two register fields, one for the source and one for the destination. It allows data to be transferred between any pair of eight-bit registers, or, provided that HL contains the right address, between any register and any cell in the store.

Arithmetic and logical operations include the 'standard set': add, add with carry, subtract, subtract with carry, AND, OR, exclusive OR, and compare. All these operations work on the accumulator, and each of the corresponding instructions has two modes: one that uses an immediate operand and one that specifies a register or a memory cell through (H, L).

(H, L) is obviously a key element in store access. A number of instructions are provided for loading and storing its contents, and some 16-bit arithmetic can be done, using (H, L) as a 16-bit accumulator and the contents of the other '16-bit registers' (B, C) and (D, E) as operands. This makes array manipulation and multiple-length arithmetic rather simpler than on the 6800.

For input and output, the 8080 has room for 256 'ports' in either direction. Each port can carry a peripheral interface. Two special instructions are provided:

IN   n   ↑ READ THE CONTENTS OF PORT n
           ↑ TO THE ACCUMULATOR
OUT n   ↑ SEND THE CONTENTS OF THE
           ↑ ACCUMULATOR TO PORT n

In practice, the input/output instructions are executed very much like the others. The port number is placed on the address bus just as if it were a memory address, but a special bus line asserts that an I/O operation is being carried out. This scheme allows the address-selection mechanism on each peripheral interface to be very much simpler, involving at most eight address lines and an 'I/O operation line'. The drawback is that the IN and OUT instructions cannot be index modified, and they cannot use indirection, so that it is not at all easy to handle large numbers of peripherals as arrays. Of course, it is always possible to put the peripherals into the main address space and to ignore the IN and OUT instructions altogether.

For handling interrupts, the 8080 provides for up to eight different interrupt routines, compared with two on the 6800. The interrupt-calling mechanism is somewhat more complex, and requires the device to force a subroutine call instruction on to the data lines at the moment when the system would normally be reading the next instruction from the store. However, interrupt control chips are available that simplify this procedure.

Clearly, the 8080 satisfies the eight essential requirements listed in Chapter 5, and is therefore a viable microprocessor. Its advantages over the 6800 include better array manipulation, easier double-length working, and automatic calculation of parity. On the other hand, simple programs tend to be somewhat longer because of the size of the jump instructions and the need to manipulate (H,L) for many memory accesses, and the management of interrupts is more complex. In summary, neither system has any really outstanding general advantages, and the main factor in choosing between them for any application could well be the prior experience and knowledge of the design engineers.

Some more general features

In practice, every microprocessor on sale now satisfies the eight essential points listed in Chapter 5, and most of them have features that correspond to the desirable aspects listed there as well. However, microprocessors differ from each other in several different ways, each of which makes a particular device more or less suitable for a specific job.

Word size

Most microprocessors use one-bit, four-bit, eight-bit or 16-bit words, although there are a few with intermediate word sizes such as 10 or 12. In general, the cost of a system increases steadily with the number of bits used, so it often pays to match the system carefully against its application.

One-bit microprocessors are used chiefly as controllers for very simple systems such as gramophone turntables or change-giving machines. They can, of course, be programmed to do any calculation, but since every arithmetic function is effectively 'multiple-length' they are very slow, and the programs are long and complex. Because of these drawbacks, one-bit microprocessors are hardly ever used as general-purpose components; more often advantage is taken of their simple structure to place ROM, RAM and interface circuitry on to a single silicon chip, and to build special-purpose 'controllers' for cheap, high-volume systems.

A four-bit word is the right size to hold a single decimal digit. Four-bit microprocessors therefore are chiefly used to implement calculators, weighing machines, telephone dialling systems and other devices that make heavy use of decimal digits and where speed is not important.

Systems with eight bits can handle alphanumeric information as well as decimal numbers. Their speed in arithmetic is several times higher than that of four-bit processors, and is sufficient for many control applications. These facts give eight-bit systems a good general-purpose capability, and indicate that they should be used for a wide range of problems. At the lower end, the range is bounded by the availability of a cheaper four-bit or one-bit system that will do the job as well. At the upper limit, there are certain problems in which an eight-bit processor cannot do the necessary arithmetic fast enough. The eight-bit word seems likely to establish itself as the microprocessor standard, to be used unless there is a good reason for the contrary. It is interesting to note that the 'hobby market', which is concerned with machines powerful enough to do general-purpose computing and yet cheap enough for individual people to buy privately, has so far concentrated mainly on eight-bit machines.

Sixteen-bit systems are the 'large machines' of the microprocessor world. They tend to be expensive, and their main advantage is that they are usually capable of fast arithmetic. This is specially true of those models – like the Texas 9900 – that are fitted with instructions for multiplication and division.

Some 16-bit microprocessors use the same order codes as established minicomputers. One such is the LSI 11, which can be seen as an extension of the DEC PDP-11 computer range. This compatibility means that all the software developed for the minicomputers can be used on the microprocessor without modification. This factor can be an overriding reason for the selection of a particular device.

Number of pins

In designing an integrated circuit, there are strong technological reasons for reducing the number of pins on any device. In general, fewer pins mean cheaper manufacture and more reliable operation.

Some manufacturers have saved on pin numbers by time-multiplexing different signals on the same pins. Thus a device with 16 bits of address and eight-bit data words may have a group of eight 'general-purpose' pins, which at different times carry a data word, or the most significant half of an address, or its least significant half. This system has two disadvantages from the system designer's point of view; it requires external chips to buffer the various items of information, and it slows down the running of the entire machine. These points should be borne in mind when selecting a microprocessor for a particular purpose.

Number of orders

The manufacturers of a microprocessor often advertise the number of orders available ('441 Distinct Instructions!!') as if it were a straightforward and reliable measure of goodness. In reality the situation is not so simple.

In a machine with a good overall architecture, the number of orders needed to give full flexibility in writing programs is surprisingly small. Many successful machines have had repertoires of only 16 different orders.

In one important way the existence of very many orders is a serious drawback. It tends to make programming more difficult, because there is far more to learn, and the programmer is always searching for different, more effective ways of coding particular algorithms.

Much advertising in this area is misguided, and it is often worth trying to see through the inflated claims to the truth behind. There are three ways of claiming that a machine has a large number of orders.

- The orders may in fact be variants of a small number of themes. For example, the ADD instruction on the 6800 can exist in four modes and can refer to either accumulator. A manufacturer might count it as eight distinct orders, but conceptually it is only one.
- A machine might have a number of complex orders that fulfil certain very common tasks, such as moving whole blocks of data, comparing strings of characters, controlling the protocol for data transmission, or converting between decimal and binary. These orders can be regarded as built-in subroutines and are often extremely useful. They can also be ignored if the application does not call for their use.
- The architecture of a machine might be so bad that large numbers of orders are needed to make it work at all. To give two examples, a machine without a carry register would need a 'ghost add' instruction: 'Set the accumulator to 1 if adding X and Y would have set the carry; otherwise set the accumulator to 0'. Again, a machine with 15-bit addresses, which used a store with 2^{16} locations, would need a complete duplicate set of instructions for referring to the upper half of the store.

In practice, any of these three reasons may apply in combination. When selecting a system, it is always worth discovering exactly what the manufacturer means when claiming a certain number of orders. However, there is one proviso: if you cannot understand the purpose of some of the instructions after several careful readings of the manufacturer's documentation, the reason for their inclusion is probably the third, and you should drop the device from further investigation.

Speed

The effective speed of a microprocessor is not the number of clock pulses per second, but the rate at which it will do a specific job. The only way to be sure that a system is fast enough is to write the control program and measure its performance. Estimates always tend to optimism, and can be wrong by as much as ten times.

Peripheral handling

The mechanisms for handling peripherals often form the major part of the cost of any system. Before deciding on any particular microprocessor, you should know exactly how you plan to interface the various devices, how many chips are necessary, and how well the central system can service them. The following points are particularly important:

- existence and specification of interface chips;
- complexity of address selection mechanisms;
- methods of producing interrupts;
- speed of response to interrupts.

To make a fair assessment, you should be familiar with the various interfacing aids offered by rival manufacturers. It is best for the information to be present as background knowledge even before the design process starts. It pays to read component data manuals, instead of novels, when travelling on long journeys.

Programming aids

The minimum programming aid for any system is a symbolic assembler and a resident monitor. Other more advanced aids include editors, filing systems, compilers for high-level languages, simulators and debuggers. These items will be discussed in Chapters 11 and 12; but here it can be said that the more aids that are available, the easier and faster it is to get new systems developed.

No matter how good a microprocessor may be, without programming aids it cannot be used at all. The provision of these aids is therefore a key factor in microprocessor selection.

11

High-level languages

Any notation for writing programs is called a 'language'. All the programs presented so far are written in symbolic assembly language, which is characterised by being very closely linked with a particular type of processor.

A high-level language is a notation that allows an algorithm to be expressed in a more natural, 'mathematical' way. For example, one could write:

AVE := (TEMPA + TEMPB + TEMPC + TEMPD)/4

instead of:

```
LDA A, TEMPA
ADA A, TEMPB
ADA A, TEMPC
ADA A, TEMPD
ASR A
ASR A
STA A, AVE
```

or again,

IF TA − TB < 15 THEN GOTO XX

instead of

```
LDA A, TA
SUB A, TB
CMP A, #15
BMI XX
```

Most engineers are familiar with a high-level language such as BASIC or FORTRAN. Those who are not can find explanations in reference 1 or in many other good books.

High-level languages offer three advantages over symbolic assembly code:

- An assembly-language program is verbose and difficult to read. It is totally incomprehensible to anyone not familiar with the intimate details of the processor involved. In contrast, a program written in a high-level language is usually compact, and is far easier to follow; it helps to make programming appear to be less of a black art.
- An assembly-language program can only be used on one specific type of processor. On the other hand, a program written in a high-level language will run on any processor equipped with the right support software. High-level language programs are *transportable*.
- Assembly-code programs are difficult and time-consuming to write. High-level language programs can be written and tested much faster, and are easier to maintain and update. Factors of up to ten in writing speed have been reported.

Eventually we shall consider two particular high-level languages — BASIC and PL/F. First, however, we shall discuss the means by which programs written in these languages are actually run on a microcomputer.

Compilers

A compiler is a program that reads a text in a high-level language and translates it into the binary code of some 'target' microprocessor. The compiler does a job analogous to that of a symbolic assembler, but it is a more complicated program, because a high-level language is more remote from binary than is assembly code.

A compiler is generally obliged to use fairly inflexible means of translation, and the binary code it generates for a given algorithm is never as fast or as compact as it would be if written by an experienced and strongly motivated human programmer. In the case of a good, well designed compiler the code might take 50 per cent more space in the store and be up to 70 per cent slower in execution. Some compilers give results that are very much worse. On the other hand, little code is actually written by perfect programmers, and comparing average performances, the compiler's efficiency is seen to be acceptable.

The various stages involved in writing and running a program with the aid of a compiler are shown in *Figure 11.1*.

- First, the program is written and keypunched on to a machine-readable medium such as a floppy disk, paper tape or cards.
- Next, the program is compiled to produce a binary version. The binary code is also in machine-readable form, usually on a disk or paper tape.

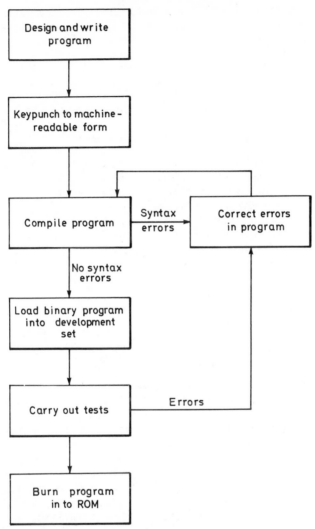

Figure 11.1

- Next, the binary program is loaded into a 'development set', which is a microprocessor with RAM, teletype and I/O ports that can simulate the operations of the system being designed. Here the program is tested to ensure that it works. As the mistakes emerge, the original program is corrected and the whole process is repeated as many times as necessary.

- Finally, when the program is believed correct, the binary version is burned into read-only memory, which is then installed in the system being built.

The time for one cycle of this process depends crucially on the equipment available. If the source text is on a floppy disk, it can be corrected very quickly by an 'editor' program. Cards are also fast to alter, but a program on paper tape is slow to edit as the tape has to be copied from beginning to end.

The compilation can also be done in three ways:

- On a terminal linked to a remote bureau computer through a teletype. This is slow and very expensive.
- On a local minicomputer. This is convenient if a minicomputer with the right compiler is available.
- On the microprocessor development set itself. This is only possible if the set has enough RAM to run the compiler (normally at least 32K bytes) and a rich set of peripherals, including a printer and a floppy disk system.

Interpreters

When a program is *compiled*, it is translated into binary machine code once and for all, before it is run. On the other hand, a program being *interpreted* is always stored in its original written form, as a series of characters. As each instruction of the program is obeyed, it is first decoded or 'interpreted' to discover what it means. If an instruction is part of a loop so that it is obeyed many times, it is also deciphered many times over. This makes programs being interpreted hundreds of times slower than those that are compiled beforehand.

Figure 11.2 shows the process of running an interpreted program. The program is written and then keypunched directly into the development set. The set already contains the interpreter program that is responsible for deciphering and executing the program being tested.

As soon as the program has been keyed in, it can be started and its behaviour observed. At any point, it can be stopped, corrected and restarted just by typing the corrections on the development set terminal. When correct, it is recorded on read-only memory together with the interpreter program, and then loaded into the system being built.

Interpretive systems allow cycles of tests and corrections to be made much more quickly than even the best systems based on compilers. This is sometimes an overriding advantage.

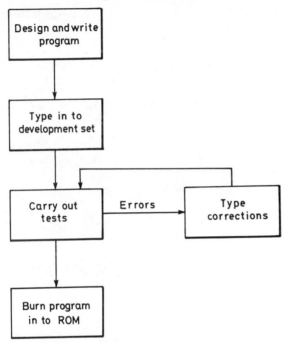

Figure 11.2

```
10 PRINT "INCOME","TAX DUE"
20 FOR I=500 TO 10000 STEP 500
30 LET T=0
40 IF I < 1470 THEN 80
50 LET T=T+0.32*(I-1470)
60 IF I < 6470 THEN 80
65 REMARK : 0.53 IN NEXT LINE = (85%-32%)
70 LET T=T+0.53*(I-6470)
80 PRINT I,T
90 NEXT I
100 END
OK
```

Figure 11.3

BASIC

BASIC is a very simple high-level language originally designed for mathematical calculations, and nearly always supported by an *interpreter*. It uses 'scientific notation' to handle numbers of any reasonable size without danger of overflow. The example given in *Figure 11.3* is a sufficient illustration of the language. It prints a table of annual income tax payable on the following assumptions:

First £1470: tax free
Next £5000: tax at 32 per cent
Any further income: tax at 85 per cent

The output of this program is shown in *Figure 11.4*.

INCOME	TAX DUE
500	0
1000	0
1500	9.6
2000	169.6
2500	329.6
3000	489.6
3500	649.6
4000	809.6
4500	969.6
5000	1129.6
5500	1289.6
6000	1449.6
6500	1625.5
7000	2050.5
7500	2475.5
8000	2900.5
8500	3325.5
9000	3750.5
9500	4175.5
10000	4600.5

Figure 11.4

In its original form, BASIC was unsuitable for direct control of peripheral devices. Most microprocessor versions, however, provide certain extensions that make it feasible to write real-time control programs in BASIC. In one version, the extra facilities allow the data and status words of peripherals to be read and written directly. Thus

LET J = PEEK (61148)

will read the contents of the cell at location 61148 (which happens to be F008 in hex) and loads its value into variable J; similarly,

POKE   (61149, 1)

will send the value 1 to cell 61149.

A further essential feature is that the system allows the logical operations AND, OR and NOT between variables, and delivers the same results as if the values had been stored as two's complement binary numbers.

BASIC is particularly useful when extensive mathematical calculations are involved, and where the speed of response is not a critical factor. This is illustrated in the following example. (The details of the example are fictitious, but the idea is based on a surveying instrument produced by Hewlett-Packard Ltd.)

A microcomputer controls a radar-based range-finding instrument. At a command from the microprocessor the device transmits a pulse of radar waves aimed at a remote object, and starts a 16-bit counter. The counter runs at 150 MHz until an echo is received, or until the counter overflows. The contents of the counter then indicate the distance of the object, in units of one metre. A value of zero shows that no echo was received.

In practice, readings of this kind can be affected by noise, and are often wrong. The instrument therefore makes a large number of measurements, discards those that seem spurious, and finds the average of the remainder.

To make a measurement the surveyor points the instrument at the target and presses the 'run' button. The microprocessor then takes over and does the following steps:

- The machine tries to make 100 distinct measurements, not counting those that return no echo. The measurements are stored in an array. To stop the system from getting stuck in a loop if it happens to be mis-aligned and unable to find an echo at all, the number of unsuccessful trials is counted. When it reaches 50, the run is stopped and a warning message appears on the control screen:

"TARGET NOT RETURNING ECHO"

- Suppose that the system has succeeded in getting 100 independent readings of the distance. Most of them are due to genuine echoes, but some may be spurious. Suppose it is known that all genuine readings must be within four metres of one another. The machine calculates the difference between the extreme values amongst its readings. If the difference is four metres or less, all is well and it can accept every value as genuine. Otherwise it finds and discards the value most remote from the current average and repeats the analysis on the readings still left.

- Finally, the system works out the mean of the remaining values and displays it, together with a count of the number of values discarded. This gives the surveyor an idea of the quality of his observation. A typical display would read:

DISTANCE = 1437.3 METRES
18 POINTS DISCARDED

The interface to the system has the layout shown in *Figure 11.5*. The control program, in BASIC, is shown in *Figure 11.6*.

Address   Layout

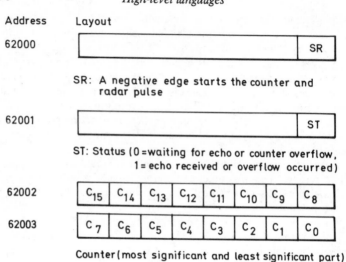

SR: A negative edge starts the counter and radar pulse

ST: Status (0 = waiting for echo or counter overflow, 1 = echo received or overflow occurred)

Counter (most significant and least significant part)

Figure 11.5

PL/F

PL/F is one of a family of high-level languages for microprocessors, based loosely on subsets of PL/I. It is supported by a compiler (or rather by a compiler for each microprocessor for which it is available) and aims to combine the advantages of a high-level language with the flexibility and efficiency of assembly coding. It achieves this target somewhat better than most other languages.

The reader can gain an impression of PL/F from the formal description in Appendix 3, and from the sample program in Appendix 4. The latter is a transcription of the teletype exchange program that formed the main topic of Chapter 7.

PL/F is well suited for the construction of large complex programs. Not only does it produce code that runs hundreds of times faster than BASIC, but it offers full facilities for *structured programming*.

'Structured programming' is the most recent name for the idea that programs should be properly designed like any other engineered product. One aspect of this notion is the presence of 'variable declarations', or statements that name variable quantities and specify their types (integer, address, or array of integers or addresses). They correspond roughly to definition or variable items in assembly language. When translating instructions the compiler rejects any names that have not previously been declared. The purpose of declarations, therefore, is to make programs easier to read, to protect them against errors caused by mis-spellings, and to ensure that types are used consistently.

```
10 REM ALL LINES WHICH START WITH REM ARE COMMENTS
20 REM PROGRAM FOR RANGE FINDER
30 REM D IS ARRAY FOR RANGE FINDER
40 DIM D(100)
50 LET C=0
60 REM LOOP FOR GETTING IN READINGS
70 FOR K=1 TO 100
80 REM SEND RADAR PULSE AND START COUNTER
90 POKE (62000,1)
100 POKE(62000,0)
110 REM NOW WAIT FOR ECHO
120 LET J=PEEK(62001)
130 IF J=0 THEN 120
140 REM ECHO RECEIVED, READ (16-BIT) VALUE IN COUNTER
150 D(K)=256*PEEK(62002)+PEEK(62003)
160 REM JUMP IF NOT ZERO
170 IF D(K) > 0 THEN 230
180 REM COUNT UNSUCCESSFUL ATTEMPTS IN C
190 LET C=C+1
200 IF C < 50 THEN 90
210 PRINT"TARGET NOT RETURNING ECHO"
220 STOP
230 NEXT K
240 REM NOW WE HAVE 100 GOOD READINGS
250 REM X IS USED TO COUNT NUMBER OF REJECTED READINGS
260 LET X=0
270 REM NEXT SECTION CALCULATES MEAN OF REMAINING
280 REM READINGS IN M, AND RANGE (DIFFERENCE BETWEEN
290 REM LOWEST AND HIGHEST) IN R, DISQUALIFIED
300 REM READINGS ARE REPRESENTED AS 0
305 LET M=0
310 LET A=0
315 LET T=0
320 LET B=10000
330 FOR K=1 TO 20
340 IF D(K)=0 THEN 400
350 LET M=M+D(K)
355 LET T=T+1
360 IF D(K)< A THEN 380
370 LET A=D(K)
380 IF D(K) > B THEN 400
390 LET B=D(K)
400 NEXT K
405 LET M=M/T
410 LET R=A-B
420 REM NOW TEST R, IF R=4 OR LESS, THEN ALL REMAINING READINGS
430 REM GOOD.
435 IF R <= 4 THEN 580
440 REM ELSE FIND AND DISCARD READING MOST REMOTE FROM M
450 LET A=0
460 LET B=0
470 FOR K= 1 TO 100
480 IF D(K)= 0 THEN 520
490 IF ABS(D(K) - M) < A THEN 520
500 LET A = ABS(D(K) - M)
510 LET B=K
520 NEXT K
530 LET D(B) = 0
540 LET X = X+1
550 REM TAKE OFF EXTREME VALUE, COUNT, AND TRY AGAIN
560 GOTO 300
570 REM HERE RESULT IS DISPLAYED
580 PRINT "DISTANCE IS";M
590 PRINT "NUMBER OF REJECTED READINGS IS";X
600 STOP
?
```

Figure 11.6

One vital feature of any structured program is that it should be built as a collection of sub-assemblies, each with a well-defined function and interfaced to the other components. This notion was fully discussed in Chapter 7, which suggested that the sub-assemblies should be implemented by subroutines.

In PL/F, subroutines are called *procedures*. The structure of a procedure is more formal (and therefore more easily checked) than that of a machine-code subroutine. There are two important structural differences:

Formal parameters. Most subroutines have at least one *parameter*, or quantity that is handed over to the subroutine for it to do its work. In our example, subroutine TSERVE, each time it is called, looks after a particular terminal line. The number of the line concerned is handed over as a parameter. The assembly-code version relies on passing it in an informal way by using one of the accumulators, but the PL/F procedure receives the line number as a *formal* parameter, called LN. This is made clear in the procedure heading (which defines the procedure's interface) and in the declaration that follows.

Block structure and local variables. Many variables in programming are associated with particular subroutines, and it would be an error for them to be used by other parts of the program. When a program is written by one person alone this mistake is improbable, but when several people collaborate the risk is real, particularly if some of them (like the author) tend to use short names such as 'J', 'K', or 'X'.

In a block-structured program each declaration has a 'scope' or area of validity that may be less than the program as a whole. For example, the variables declared in a procedure can be used only in that procedure, and any attempt to refer to those variables from outside is treated as an error by the compiler. The area of program over which a variable is valid is called a 'block'. Outside a block the variable does not exist, and indeed the name can safely be used for another purpose.

One kind of block is a procedure; but blocks can also be delimited by the system words DO; . . . END; Blocks may be nested like Russian dolls. In particular, the whole program is a block, and variables declared at the head of the program are accessible everywhere. They are called 'global variables'.

The name 'structured programming' has become associated with certain methods of sequence control. It is now widely accepted that the control of sequence by labels and 'goto' instructions is harmful and leads to incomprehensible and incorrect programs. Most modern high-level programming languages offer alternatives to the 'goto' on the following lines:

- Any group of statements can be made into a single statement by enclosing them in the brackets DO; . . . END;
- The conditional statement that starts with an IF does not have to specify a jump or goto, as in BASIC. Instead, the test may be followed by any statement (which includes, of course, a group of statements enclosed in DO; . . . END;). Two examples that compare PL/F with BASIC will illustrate this point:

	unstructured	*structured*
(a)	110 IF X > = 0 THEN 130	IF X < 0 THEN X:= −X
	120 LET X = −X	
	130	
(b)	200 IF A <= B THEN 240	IF A > B THEN DO;
	210 LET D = B	D:= B; B:= A; A:= D;
	220 LET B = A	END;
	230 LET A = D	
	240	

The structured version is to be preferred, firstly because the test is the 'right' way if something is to be done, and secondly because there is no need to refer to the label of an instruction, which has no connection with the current part of the algorithm.

- The conditional statement can be followed by an ELSE, and an alternative course of action to be followed if the condition is false. For example:

unstructured

```
50  IF Y < 100 THEN 80
60  PRINT 'Y OVER 100'
70  GOTO 90
80  PRINT 'Y LESS THAN 100'
90
```

structured

```
IF Y < 100 THEN
    PRINT ('Y LESS THAN 100');
ELSE
    PRINT ('Y OVER 100');
```

- Repetition is invoked by the system word WHILE. This is followed by a condition and by one or more statements enclosed in DO; . . . END; brackets. The bracketed statements are repeated as long as the condition remains true. Again, two illustrations will suffice:

unstructured

```
(a)  10 LET X = 100
     20 IF X < 1 GOTO 60
     30 PRINT X
     40 LET X = X/2
     50 GOTO 20
     60
```

structured

```
X := 100
WHILE X >= 1 DO;
    PRINT (X)
    X:= ASR X
    END;
```

High-level languages

(b) 100 FOR J = 1 TO 101 STEP 10   J:= 1
     110 PRINT J   WHILE J $<=$ 101 DO;
     120 NEXT J   PRINT (J);
                                     J := J + 10 END;

(Note that the FOR statement of BASIC is actually a structured concept!)

These four constructions allow GOTOs and labels to be eliminated in almost every context, although sometimes the removal is somewhat artificial. A good practical rule for the would-be structured program is:

- *Never* use a backward GOTO, i.e. one to a place earlier in the program.
- Use a forward GOTO only if the code is genuinely simplified as a result.

Discussion

In every project, the design engineer must make a decision whether to use a high-level language, and if so of what type.

The various programming systems we have discussed can be fitted into spectra in two different dimensions. First, they affect the cost of programming, which is high for assembly language, much lower for a compiled language like PL/F, and very low for BASIC and similar systems. Secondly, they have a major influence on the cost of the system needed to fulfil a particular job. A good assembly-code program will lead to the cheapest system in terms of speed requirements and size of storage; at the other extreme, systems based on interpretive languages will be slow and relatively expensive because of the need to include a large interpreter program.

These considerations suggest that an interpretive system should be used when:

- the speed of the system being designed is not critical, and
- it is required to get a system working (possibly for demonstration purposes) in the shortest possible time.

From an economic point of view, it is also worthwhile using BASIC for systems that are to be built in very small quantities, where the programming cost overshadows the costs of individual components.

A high-level language such as PL/F speeds up programming and helps with program maintenance, at a cost of increasing store requirements by about half. The decision on whether to use a high-level language is therefore one of economics. Consider the case of a system with the following estimated costs:

	Using assembly code	Using high-level language
Programming cost (once only)	£10 000	£5 000
Unit cost/system	£100	£150

Figure 11.7 shows how the overall cost varies with the number of units produced, for both methods of programming. The curves cross at $n = 100$. This suggests that it is only worth using assembly language if the expected production is over 100 units.

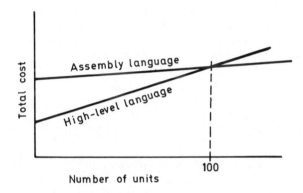

Figure 11.7

In practice, the falling cost of components is steadily pushing the point of intersection further and further to the right. The conclusion is that, although the engineer should know assembly language in order to understand the behaviour of his system, he should actually use a high-level language for all practical development.

12

Practical aids to programming

The last major task in commissioning a new microprocessor-based system consists of checking the programming. Suppose that the program is written, and the hardware of the prototype system is designed and built, so that to start working it needs only a ROM with the 'correct' program. This chapter addresses the problem of bringing the hardware and software together.

The ROM simulator

ROM simulators are used for checking systems with very small programs (say 64 instructions or less). A ROM simulator is a special-purpose microcomputer with a RAM, and three peripheral interfaces: one to a keyboard, one to a PROM programmer and one to the system being tested. This last interface is made with a plug that gives direct memory access to the simulator's RAM, and that has the same pin allocations and voltage levels as a standard ROM chip, so that for the device being tested the store of the ROM simulator *appears* to be a read-only memory.

To set up the program, the engineer translates it manually into binary or hexadecimal notation, and enters it into the ROM simulator store, using the keyboard.

Next, the ROM simulator is plugged in to the new machine in place of the eventual ROM chip, and the device is switched on and tried out. It behaves exactly as it would do if a genuine ROM chip were plugged in, and executes the program it reads from the simulator.

At this point, faults in the program begin to come to light. Once a particular fault has been observed, it is usually easy to find the program mistake that caused it, particularly if the help of an experienced programmer can be found. Some errors can be corrected by changing individual words in the simulator, but others will require the entire program to be rewritten.

Eventually, the system is found to behave correctly under all conditions. At this point, a new PROM chip is plugged in to the PROM programmer interface, and an exact copy of the contents of the ROM simulator store is automatically burned into it. Finally, the simulator is removed from the system and the PROM chip fitted in its place. The system is now complete.

Unfortunately this method only works for small programs because it is almost impossible to translate large programs by hand correctly. More complex systems need a set of tools, some software and some hardware, for commissioning and testing.

The software tools are programs that — in principle — can be run on any computer system with enough store to support them. As mentioned in Chapter 11, this could be a remote bureau machine, or a local minicomputer, or a microprocessor development set with a large store and a floppy disk system. The precise details of the many systems in existence vary greatly, and the sections that follow are intended to convey only the general principles of these tools.

Filing systems

A filing system is an orderly way of keeping information on a permanent store like a floppy disk. Most filing systems allow the user to keep 'documents'. Each document is a stream of characters of arbitrary length; it could, for example, be a program or a poem or a list of names and addresses or a circular letter. Every document is given its own unique identifying name.

A filing system must be supported by software that allows that retrieval of named documents whenever they are needed, the construction of new documents, the removal of old, unwanted ones and the scavenging or collection of the storage space freed by this removal. The file support software is usually incorporated into the programs that use the filing system, so the user need make no special effort to ensure that it is there.

The most common way of setting up a new document is to type it on a terminal keyboard. When the computer has been started up, it will initiate a dialogue somewhat on these lines (the machine's contribution is in lower case letters, the user's in capitals):

```
function?    NEWDOC
name?        FIREALARM
TITLE  "FIRE ALARM PROGRAM"
```

```
...
...  ⎞   Text of
...  ⎬   new document
...  ⎠
```

START HERE

****   Marker to show end of document

ok

Often new documents can also be read from cards, paper tape, cassettes or other floppy disks.

Editors

An editor is a program that allows a document, already in the filing system, to be altered.

It is technically difficult to make changes to parts of a document while leaving other parts untouched. One common system of editing therefore relies on reading the old, 'source' document from beginning to end and using the data to generate a completely new one. Again, the system is interactive and uses a dialogue. In one typical system, facilities are provided to copy or skip the old document for so many characters, or so many lines, or up to a particular sequence of characters. New material can also be inserted, and specified sequences of characters can be amended.

Consider a document called 'WENCESLAS' with the following text:

GOOD KING WENCESLUS LOOKED OUT
ON THE FEAST OF
WHEN THE SNOW LAY ROUND ABOUT
DEEP AND CRSIP AND EEEVEN
THOUGH THE FROST WAS CRUEL
WHEN A POOR MAN CAME IN SIGHT
WITH A POT OF GRUEL

This could be corrected by:

function?	EDIT	
name?	WENCESLAS	
'LUS'='LAS'		Correct spelling
C 'OF'		Copy to end of 'of'
I ' STEPHEN'		Insert (space) STEPHEN
'CRSIP'='CRISP'		Correct spelling
'EEE'='E'		Correct spelling
C1		Copy to end of current line

I 'BRIGHTLY SHONE THE MOON THAT NIGHT
'
                    Insert extra line (with newline at end)
C2   Copy two lines
S1   Skip one line
I 'GATHERING WINTER FUEL
'
                    Insert extra line (with newline at end)
****

Regrettably there is no standardisation among editors; every one is different in detail. Some editors offer complex and powerful facilities for repeating a given change through the whole of a text or interchanging two paragraphs; but two marks of a really effective editor are:

- The editor should be simple to use; there should be a 'minimal' subset of perhaps two or three different commands that allow all editing to be done, even if in a roundabout way. In practice, a design engineer is likely to use an editor intensively for a few weeks, and then to spend several months on different work before the need arises to use the editor again. Over this period of time, detailed knowledge of complex commands is likely to evaporate, so that an editor that needs only a few simple orders is at considerable advantage.
- The editor should be safe; that is, there should be no risk of losing a document entirely if the system breaks down during an editing session.

Subroutine libraries

If a microprocessor system is of any size, it is unlikely that all its components are original; in all probability other programs with similar components have already been written.

A great help to programming is a *subroutine library*, which contains well tested and documented versions of common program components. A good library would include subroutines in the following areas:

Arithmetic	Multiplication, division, multiple-length operations, floating point ('scientific notation') facilities.
Algebraic functions	Square roots, logs, exponentials, trigonometric and inverse trigonometric functions.
Matrix algebra	Various matrix manipulations, including solution of simultaneous equations.

Fourier transforms	For conversions between time and frequency domains.
Sorting	Subroutines for putting arrays into order.
Input and output	Decimal-binary conversion, display, and reading numbers from keyboards.
Filing functions	Software needed to use the filing systems.
Peripheral control	Interface software for supporting cassette tapes, floppy disks, synchronous and asynchronous data transmission.
Operating systems	General-purpose systems for controlling interrupts and ensuring timely response to external events.
System tests	Programs that test the system and generate warnings if errors are detected.

The subroutines in a library are kept as documents, usually in source form: assembly code or a high-level language.

Translators (compilers and assemblers)

Many points about compilers and assemblers have already been covered in previous chapters. Here we shall mainly consider the way in which these translators fit in with other programming tools.

A translator will normally accept a document in the file store as its source text. The name of the document is specified in a dialogue, as follows:

function?   ASSEMBLE
name?   FIREALARM

The translator should allow the source program to nominate its own library subroutines and include them automatically. For instance, a program that uses certain mathematical functions might run as follows:

```
TITLE "REACTOR CONTROL"
.=1000
*INCLUDE MULTIPLY      )MULTIPLY, DIVIDE and SQUARE-
*INCLUDE DIVIDE        }ROOT are the names of library routines
*INCLUDE SQUAREROOT    )
. . .
. . .
JSR   SQUAREROOT        ↑ CALL SQUAREROOT SUBROUTINE
. . .
. . .
```

JSR DIVIDE   ↑ CALL DIVIDE SUBROUTINE
. . .
. . .

This facility is sometimes provided to several depths, so that library subroutines can themselves nominate other subroutines for inclusion. However, care must be taken not to include any subroutine more than once.

Many translators are equipped with *macro generators*. A macro is a short segment of text that can be inserted at any point in a program. A macro is not part of a library but must be defined in the program that uses it, and it is not normally a subroutine. The following example will make this clear.

Consider a program, like the one in Chapter 7, that uses arrays and index modification. It needs a set of instructions to add an accumulator to the index register. In Chapter 7, this sequence was made into a subroutine called AA. It could also have been made into a macro, thus:

```
MACRO     AA          ↑ MACRO TO ADD ACC B
   STX    AAB         ↑ TO INDEX REGISTER
   ADD    B, AAC
   STA    B, AAC
   BCC    .+5         ↑ THIS MEANS: SKIP NEXT
   INC    AAB         ↑ INSTRUCTION IF C CLEAR
   LDX    AAB
END MACRO
```

Elsewhere in the program, the sequence could be used by writing its name as a 'pseudo-instruction'. For example:

```
TSERVE:   TAB
          ASL  B
          ASL  B
          LDX  #?F100
          AA                ↑ GET ADDRESS OF INTERFACE
          LDA  A, X(3)
```

This appears very similar to the subroutine call in Chapter 7. The difference is that the *whole* text of the macro is inserted at every point where its name, AA, is mentioned. This makes the program a little faster (since the subroutine entry and exit instructions are no longer needed) and a great deal longer — over 100 words in the teletype exchange program. Macros are expensive, and great care should be employed in their use.

Translators have two forms of output. One is a printed listing, and the other is a binary program suitable for loading and running in the target machine.

When necessary, the listing should be as extensive and detailed as possible. It should show the source program, the result of the translation (perhaps in hex) and a list of symbols together with their values. However, such a full listing will take time to produce on a slow printer, and may not always be necessary; for example, details of standard library routines could well be omitted. It is therefore common practice to allow all or part of the listing to be suppressed.

One flexible method of listing control is to make the translator send the listing to a file rather than to a printer. The 'listing document' can then be printed selectively, choosing only those parts of it that are actually of interest.

The binary program must, of course, be in machine-readable form. If the translator is running on the development system itself, the binary program will be set up as a document in the floppy disk file. Otherwise the binary program must be transferred to the development set, and this can be done by recording it on a cassette, punching it on paper tape, or transmitting it directly over a communication line.

All these methods are liable to error. A mechanical error at this stage would cause the engineer to start testing a program that was both incorrect and different from the translator listing. Such mistakes are hard to find, and can waste much time. Most practical systems avoid them by two methods:

- Each character of the binary program output is given a particular parity, so that the loss of a single bit can be detected.
- Each group or 'block' of characters includes a 'check sum'. This is a number calculated by adding together the numerical values of all the characters in the block. When the binary program is loaded into the development set, the check sum is recalculated independently and checked. Any character that was corrupted or completely lost in transmission will show up as a discrepancy.

Some program development systems allow the user to construct programs where the various components are written in different languages — perhaps some in assembly code, some in PL/F and some in FORTRAN. This facility is likely to be useful in the construction of very large programs from components obtained from various different sources.

To make the facility possible at all, the components have to be combined after translation. Each of the several translators must therefore do its work without 'knowing' exactly where in the store of the target machine the code being produced is destined to run. All the translators in such a system must generate code in a much more complicated general format called 'relocatable binary'.

Where this can be done, library subroutines are sometimes stored in relocatable binary instead of their original source language. This allows them to be incorporated in programs of any language, and saves them from being translated afresh every time they are used. On the other hand, a subroutine available only in relocatable binary cannot easily be studied or altered, and the use of such a subroutine implies a high degree of trust in its original programmer.

Loaders

The loader is a program that runs on a development set, and reads in a new binary program ready for testing. Depending on circumstances the loader may read from paper tape, a floppy disk, or a communication line.

Loaders are usually simple programs (less than 100 instructions) and are stored permanently in ROMs. Loaders for relocatable binary code, however, are rather more complex.

Monitors

A monitor is a simple program that allows the designer to communicate with the development set. It is stored in a ROM, and entered automatically when the system is started. The detailed description below is based on Motorola's MIKBUG monitor for the 6800.

The monitor assumes that the system has a quantity of RAM, a device for reading binary programs (perhaps as paper tape) and a terminal with a display and keyboard. All communication is in hexadecimal. When the monitor is waiting for the user to take the next action, it types a dot on a new line as a 'prompt'.

The user has three basic options:

- he can inspect the contents of any store location;
- he can alter the contents of any store location;
- he can make the system jump to program at any given address.

To inspect a word of store, the user types an 'M' followed by a four-digit hex address. The monitor replies with the contents, thus (user's typing is underlined):

M 0010   97

To alter a word, the user types the same command, but follows the machine's reply by the new value. To record the value F0 in word 0017, he would type:

M 0017   3E   F0

Note that 3E is the irrelevant contents of 0017 *before* the alteration.

To inspect or alter a group of words with consecutive addresses, all but the first can be referred to by N, instead of M and an address. For example, to inspect the words between 1A and 1D, the dialogue would be:

M 001A   3A
N 001B   74
N 001C   2B
N 001D   C4

Note that all the addresses after the first are typed by the *monitor*.

To start a program at a given location, the command is J, followed by the appropriate address. For example, on the author's system the binary loader starts at FE00 and is called by:

J FE00

The monitor is the frontline of attack for testing programs. If used wisely and logically it is highly effective, but otherwise it can be a time-wasting, frustrating and infuriating experience.

There are three key rules in testing a program:

- Make sure that the program is well structured, and that the interfaces between the various components are clearly defined. If you are asked to test someone else's program that is not well structured, refuse.
- Ensure that the 'area of doubt' at any time is as small as possible — say not more than 40 instructions. The 'area of doubt' is the part of the program that is about to be tried. If this part uses any subroutines, those subroutines must be tested first. The advantage of this rule is that if the trial does not produce the expected results, the fault must have occurred in a limited area and will be easy to find by inspecting the source code.
- Keep a careful log of the trials, and write down all the mistakes you find. At frequent intervals — say every two or three errors — correct the *source* code and re-translate your program.

The actual method of testing differs slightly between assembly code programs and those written in a high-level language. First, we discuss assembly code.

Suppose that you have written your program and have spent some time reading through it to remove any obvious error. It has been translated into binary, and no crude mistakes such as illegal mnemonics or the misuse of labels have been reported. The program is now loaded into the development set and you are ready to start testing.

The first parts of the program to be tested should be the subroutines. The monitor can be used to set up small 'driver programs' that check them out and verify their correct operation. As an example, consider the subroutine AA (taken from Chapter 7):

```
AA: STX  AAB
     ADD B, AAC
     STA B, AAC
     BCC  AAD
     INC  AAB
     LDX  AAB
     RTS
```

This subroutine is supposed to add the contents of B to the index register. A 'driver' for the subroutine would be:

```
LDX  #X          ↑ SET UP INITIAL CONTENTS OF INDEX
                     REGISTER
LDA B, #Y        ↑ SET UP CONTENTS OF B REGISTER
JSR  AA          ↑ CALL SUBROUTINE
STX  0           ↑ STORE RESULT
SWI              ↑ RETURN TO MONITOR
```

This sequence sets up suitable initial values in the index register and in accumulator B, and then calls AA. The result is recorded in cells 0 and 1, where it can be inspected. SWI is a special command that returns control to the monitor.

Suppose that the first test values for X and Y are 0111 and 12 respectively. The assembler indicates that the address of AA is 2019. Hand-translation of the driver sequence (using tables) gives:

```
CE   01 11       (LDX   #?0111)
C6   12          (LDA   B,#?12
BD   20 19       (JSR   ?2019)
DF   00 00       (STX   ?0000)
3F               (SWI        )
```

The assembler also shows that the area of store from 1000 onwards is empty. It can be used for the driver program, as follows:

.M	1000	FF	CE	
.N	1001	FF	01	
.N	1002	FF	11	
.N	1003	FF	C6	
.N	1004	FF	12	
.N	1005	FF	BD	
.N	1006	FF	20	
.N	1007	FF	19	
.N	1008	FF	DF	
.N	1009	FF	00	
.N	100A	FF	00	
.N	100B	FF	3F	

Load driver program. The FFs represent the previous contents of these store locations and can be ignored.

.J	1000			Jump to driver program.
.M	0000	01		Inspect results. They are correct.
.N	0001	23		

This test is not complete. There is a path through the subroutine which involves a carry and uses the INC instruction, and this path has not yet been tested. A new value for Y is chosen, and test 2 is repeated:

.M	1004	12	FE	Set new value of Y.
.J	1000			Jump to driver program.
.M	0000	02		Inspect result.
.N	0001	0F		

The designer can now be sure that routine AA is working correctly. The same approach can now be applied to all the subroutines in the program, starting with the low-level ones that are complete in themselves. In no case should a subroutine be accepted as correct unless *every* instruction in it has been executed at least once. This approach will normally work for the whole of a well-structured program.

It may happen that a fault is thought to lie somewhere inside a long sequence of instructions, but the exact place is not clear. The fault can often be localised by stopping the sequence half-way and inspecting its workspace. If all are found to be correct, the fault must lie in the second half of the sequence; otherwise it lies in the first.

The sequence can be stopped by overwriting one of the instructions with a SWI. For example, consider a sequence like:

```
        . . .
        STA  A, XXB
PQ:     LDA  B, ZZC
        . . .
```

If PQ is known to be at location 0203, the sequence can be stopped there by:

<u>M</u> <u>0203</u>   D6   <u>3F</u>   Replace LDA B by SWI

When this sequence is next texted, it will return control to the monitor when it gets to 0203. When the workspace has been examined, the original instruction in 0203 must be replaced by typing:

<u>M</u> <u>0203</u>   3F   <u>D6</u>

Sometimes, these simple methods of testing do not work. Subroutines seem to be correct when tested by themselves, but the program as a whole jumps out of control. This type of fault is hard to find; a good way to begin is to work down the following checklist:

● Ensure that your program does not use workspace also used by the monitor.
● Ensure that all variables are given correct initial values. Failure to initialise is a common reason for subroutines working when tested once, but not when used repeatedly.
● Ensure that your stack pointer is set, and that your stack is not over-writing other data.
● Ensure that different routines are not using the same work area in an undisciplined way.
● Run some tests on the hardware of the development system. Inexplicable faults could, for example, be caused by a 'dud' storage location in the stack area.

If the checklist offers no help, it may be that you have misunderstood some aspect of the microprocessor you are using. To give an extreme example, you may be under the mistaken impression that the mnemonic for addition is AND. If you really believe this, you can spend hours testing a program and poring over the source code, and deduce nothing except that 'there is something wrong with the machine'. You are in a mental trap from which you cannot escape by yourself. On the other hand, another person reading your program would spot the fault immediately. In case of real difficulty it always pay to have your code examined by a colleague. Even the mental discipline of explaining why a certain section of code *must* be correct often brings to light an error in that very section.

If a fault remains totally intractable, the most powerful (and expensive) weapon is the simulator. This is described in the next section.

The testing of programs written in a high-level language and translated by a compiler follows the same basic principles. However, it should not be necessary to look at the actual code generated except in rare cases. The high-level language protects the user against many of the faults that occur in assembly language. Individual procedures can be tested by writing the necessary driver programs in the high-level language and compiling and running them separately, one after the other.

In summary, the purpose of testing should be to verify correct operation, not to find faults. This aim can be achieved only if the entire program and its test procedure are fully planned from the start. Nothing – and certainly not extensive 'testing' – can ever correct the faults of poor design.

Simulators

A simulator is a program designed to imitate the operation of a microprocessor. A binary program can be loaded into a simulator and run to produce the same result as it would do on the microprocessor itself. There are two main differences:

- The simulator runs some 10 000 times slower.
- The simulator prints out the result of *every* instruction, thus providing a blow-by-blow account of the action of the program.

Simulators are useful in tracking down obscure program faults, because they help to find the exact place where the program begins to deviate from its planned course. They are, however, expensive on paper and computer time, and because of their slowness they are useless in testing time-critical programs.

Debuggers

A debugger is a program that assists in testing programs. It provides the facilities of a monitor in more streamlined form. For example, the contents of a specified area of store can be printed out every time a certain point in the program is reached; or the suspension of a program can be made the result not only of reaching a particular instruction but of a Boolean condition involving the current data values.

Many debuggers are so complicated to use that they distract one's attention from the program being tested. Some people (including the author) prefer to use the simplest possible test system, believing it to be more effective in the long run.

De-assemblers

A de-assembler can take a binary program and convert it back into the corresponding symbolic assembly code. Some of the conversion, such as the selection of label and variable names, is arbitrary, so the translation is usually done interactively, with the user giving the various items the names he considers most suitable.

De-assemblers are used to reconstruct programs that may only be available in binary code. This is sometimes a vital step in studying and amending library programs.

Logic analysers

A logic analyser is a hardware device, and offers one of the most powerful methods of trouble-shooting a system that cannot be easily tested in any other way. It is particularly effective in solving real-time problems caused by peripherals and interrupts.

A diagram of a logic analyser is shown in *Figure 12.1*. It consists mainly of a number of registers (perhaps 32 or 64), which, for an eight-bit microcomputer with 16 bits of address, would have 24 bits. The registers are connected in cascade so that each time new data is loaded into the uppermost one, the contents of the others are shuffled down by one register, and the previous contents of the lower one are lost.

The device is connected to the main system bus. On every machine cycle, the information on the address and data lines is clocked into the uppermost register. At any instant, therefore, the bank of registers is a complete record of the last 32 or 64 bus cycles.

Another part of the analyser is called a 'trigger'. It is controlled by 24 switches, one for each address and data line. Each switch has three positions: 1, 0, and 'don't care'. The trigger circuit generates a pulse when the information on the bus corresponds to the switch settings. The circuit can be set to respond to any address, or a group of addresses, or any data value, or a group of data values, or a combination of the two. The trigger pulse stops the flow of data into the registers, and freezes them in the state they held when the trigger event occurred.

The last part of the analyser is a display that can show the contents of the registers.

One of the most difficult programming faults to find is when a microprocessor jumps out of control and starts executing part of the program where it has no right to be. There is often no clue where it jumped from.

This situation is one where the logic analyser can be of great value. The address of the instruction to which control is wrongly transferred is set as the trigger value; when the loss of control occurs, the analyser display will show exactly what occurred over the last few machine cycles. This information can easily be decoded to localise the fault. A logic analyser is like an oscilloscope, but with the vital difference that it displays events that happen *before* the trigger.

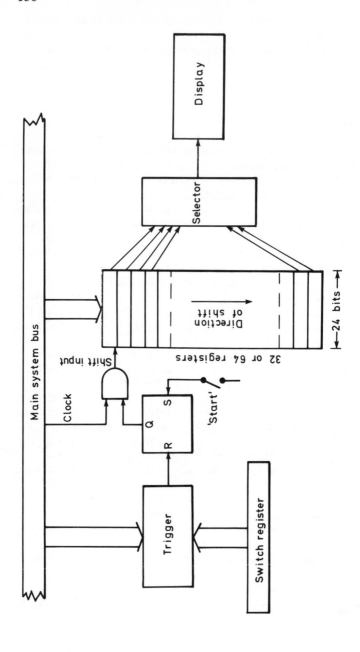

Figure 12.1

Logic analysers on the market vary in price by a range of twenty to one, but the differences are due to the method of display, to the number of storage registers, and to the sophistication of the trigger mechanism. Even the cheapest will provide the essential information needed.

Development sets

The most important tool of all is the development set itself. A set large enough to support all the software tools discussed in this chapter would need at least 32K words of store, two floppy disks and a terminal. A manufacturer's price, including software, would be about £6000. An identical configuration could be bought in the 'hobby market' for about half the price, but the software might be hard to acquire.

'Evaluation kits' costing a few hundred pounds are essentially misleading. Several thousand pounds, the price of a complete development set, is the least that can be invested to support serious design work with microprocessors.

References

Programming

1. Kemeny, J. G., and Kurtz, T. E., *Basic programming,* Wiley (1971)
2. *PL/M high-level programming manual,* INTEL Corporation (1975)
3. Barron, D. W., *Assemblers and loaders,* Macdonald (1972)
4. Dahl, O. J., Dijkstra, E. W., and Hoare, C. A. R., *Structured programming,* Academic Press (1972)
5. Jackson, M., *Principles of program design,* Academic Press (1975)
6. Barden, W., *How to program microcomputers,* Sams (1977)
7. Ogden, C. A., *Software design for microcomputers,* Prentice-Hall (1978)

Hardware

8. McGlynn, D. R., *Microprocessors—technology, architecture and applications,* Wiley (1976)
9. Healey, M., *Minicomputers and microprocessors,* Hodder and Stoughton (1976)
10. Lewin, D. W., *Theory and design of digital computers,* Nelson (1972)
11. Aspinall, D., and Dagless, E. L., *Introduction to microprocessors,* Pitman (1977)
12. Ogden, C. A., *Microcomputer design,* Prentice-Hall (1978)
13. *M6800 microcomputer system design data,* Motorola (1976)

Miscellaneous

14. Aspinall, D., *The microprocessor and its application,* Cambridge University Press (1978)
15. Weinberg, G. M., *The psychology of computer programming,* Van Nostrand Reinhold (1971)
16. Weizenbaum, J., *Computer power and human reason,* Freeman (1976)

Useful Journals

Microprocessors and Microsystems
Byte
Computer Journal

ASCII code

Group 1: Control characters

	Code	Binary equivalent
NUL	blank tape	0000000
SOH	start of heading	0000001
STX	start of text	0000010
EXT	end of text	0000011
EOT	end of transmission	0000100
ENQ	enquiry	0000101
ACK	acknowledge	0000110
BEL	bell	0000111
BS	backspace	0001000
HT	tabulate horizontally	0001001
LF	line feed	0001010
VT	tabulate vertically	0001011
FF	form feed	0001100
CR	carriage return	0001101
SO	shift out	0001110
SI	shift in	0001111
DLE	data link escape	0010000
DC1	device control 1	0010001
DC2	device control 2	0010010
DC3	device control 3	0010011
DC4	device control 4	0010100
NAK	negative acknowledge	0010101
SYN	synchronous idle	0010110
ETB	end of transmission block	0010111
CAN	cancel	0011000
EM	end of medium	0011001
SUB	substitute	0011010
ESC	escape	0011011
FS	file separator	0011100
GS	group separator	0011101
RS	record separator	0011110
US	unit separator	0011111
SP	space	0100000

Group 2: Printed characters

!	0100001	A	1000001	a	1100001
"	0100010	B	1000010	b	1100010
#	0100011	C	1000011	c	1100011
$	0100100	D	1000100	d	1100100
%	0100101	E	1000101	e	1100101
&	0100110	F	1000110	f	1100110
`	0100111	G	1000111	g	1100111
(	0101000	H	1001000	h	1101000
)	0101001	I	1001001	i	1101001
*	0101010	J	1001010	j	1101010
+	0101011	K	1001011	k	1101011
,	0101100	L	1001100	l	1101100
-	0101101	M	1001101	m	1101101
.	0101110	N	1001110	n	1101110
/	0101111	O	1001111	o	1101111
0	0110000	P	1010000	p	1110000
1	0110001	Q	1010001	q	1110001
2	0110010	R	1010010	r	1110010
3	0110011	S	1010011	s	1110011
4	0110100	T	1010100	t	1110100
5	0110101	U	1010101	u	1110101
6	0110110	V	1010110	v	1110110
7	0110111	W	1010111	w	1110111
8	0111000	X	1011000	x	1111000
9	0111001	Y	1011001	y	1111001
:	0111010	Z	1011010	z	1111010
;	0111011	[	1011011	{	1111011
<	0111100	\	1011100	|	1111100
=	0111101	]	1011101	}	1111101
>	0111110	^	1011110	~	1111110
?	0111111	—	1011111	DEL	1111111
@	1000000	'	1100000	(delete)	

Motorola 6800 instruction repertoire

The tables on pages 164–169 are reproduced by courtesy of Motorola Semiconductor Products Inc.

ACCUMULATOR AND MEMORY INSTRUCTIONS

OPERATIONS	MNEMONIC	IMMED OP	~	#	DIRECT OP	~	#	INDEX OP	~	#	EXTND OP	~	#	IMPLIED OP	~	#	BOOLEAN/ARITHMETIC OPERATION (All register labels refer to contents)	H	I	N	Z	V	C
Add	ADDA	8B	2	2	9B	3	2	AB	5	2	BB	4	3				A + M → A	↕	•	↕	↕	↕	↕
	ADDB	CB	2	2	DB	3	2	EB	5	2	FB	4	3				B + M → B	↕	•	↕	↕	↕	↕
Add Acmltrs	ABA													1B	2	1	A + B → A	↕	•	↕	↕	↕	↕
Add with Carry	ADCA	89	2	2	99	3	2	A9	5	2	B9	4	3				A + M + C → A	↕	•	↕	↕	↕	↕
	ADCB	C9	2	2	D9	3	2	E9	5	2	F9	4	3				B + M + C → B	↕	•	↕	↕	↕	↕
And	ANDA	84	2	2	94	3	2	A4	5	2	B4	4	3				A · M → A	•	•	↕	↕	R	•
	ANDB	C4	2	2	D4	3	2	E4	5	2	F4	4	3				B · M → B	•	•	↕	↕	R	•
Bit Test	BITA	85	2	2	95	3	2	A5	5	2	B5	4	3				A · M	•	•	↕	↕	R	•
	BITB	C5	2	2	D5	3	2	E5	5	2	F5	4	3				B · M	•	•	↕	↕	R	•
Clear	CLR							6F	7	2	7F	6	3				00 → M	•	•	R	S	R	R
	CLRA													4F	2	1	00 → A	•	•	R	S	R	R
	CLRB													5F	2	1	00 → B	•	•	R	S	R	R
Compare	CMPA	81	2	2	91	3	2	A1	5	2	B1	4	3				A − M	•	•	↕	↕	↕	↕
	CMPB	C1	2	2	D1	3	2	E1	5	2	F1	4	3				B − M	•	•	↕	↕	↕	↕
Compare Acmltrs	CBA													11	2	1	A − B	•	•	↕	↕	↕	↕
Complement, 1's	COM							63	7	2	73	6	3				M̄ → M	•	•	↕	↕	R	S
	COMA													43	2	1	Ā → A	•	•	↕	↕	R	S
	COMB													53	2	1	B̄ → B	•	•	↕	↕	R	S
Complement, 2's (Negate)	NEG							60	7	2	70	6	3				00 − M → M	•	•	↕	↕	①	②
	NEGA													40	2	1	00 − A → A	•	•	↕	↕	①	②
	NEGB													50	2	1	00 − B → B	•	•	↕	↕	①	②
Decimal Adjust, A	DAA													19	2	1	Converts Binary Add. of BCD Characters into BCD Format	•	•	↕	↕	↕	③
Decrement	DEC							6A	7	2	7A	6	3				M − 1 → M	•	•	↕	↕	④	•
	DECA													4A	2	1	A − 1 → A	•	•	↕	↕	④	•
	DECB													5A	2	1	B − 1 → B	•	•	↕	↕	④	•
Exclusive OR	EORA	88	2	2	98	3	2	A8	5	2	B8	4	3				A⊕M → A	•	•	↕	↕	R	•
	EORB	C8	2	2	D8	3	2	E8	5	2	F8	4	3				B⊕M → B	•	•	↕	↕	R	•
Increment	INC							6C	7	2	7C	6	3				M + 1 → M	•	•	↕	↕	⑤	•
	INCA													4C	2	1	A + 1 → A	•	•	↕	↕	⑤	•
	INCB													5C	2	1	B + 1 → B	•	•	↕	↕	⑤	•
Load Acmltr	LDAA	86	2	2	96	3	2	A6	5	2	B6	4	3				M → A	•	•	↕	↕	R	•
	LDAB	C6	2	2	D6	3	2	E6	5	2	F6	4	3				M → B	•	•	↕	↕	R	•
Or, Inclusive	ORAA	8A	2	2	9A	3	2	AA	5	2	BA	4	3				A + M → A	•	•	↕	↕	R	•
	ORAB	CA	2	2	DA	3	2	EA	5	2	FA	4	3				B + M → B	•	•	↕	↕	R	•
Push Data	PSHA													36	4	1	A → MSP, SP − 1 → SP	•	•	•	•	•	•
	PSHB													37	4	1	B → MSP, SP − 1 → SP	•	•	•	•	•	•
Pull Data	PULA													32	4	1	SP + 1 → SP, MSP → A	•	•	•	•	•	•
	PULB																						

Operation	Mnemonic	IMMED OP	~	#	DIRECT OP	~	#	INDEX OP	~	#	EXTEND OP	~	#	IMPLIED OP	~	#	Boolean/Arithmetic Operation	H	I	N	Z	V	C
Rotate Left	ROL							69	7	2	79	6	3				M	•	•	↕	↕	⑥	↕
	ROLA													49	2	1	A	•	•	↕	↕	⑥	↕
	ROLB													59	2	1	B	•	•	↕	↕	⑥	↕
Rotate Right	ROR							66	7	2	76	6	3				M	•	•	↕	↕	⑥	↕
	RORA													46	2	1	A	•	•	↕	↕	⑥	↕
	RORB													56	2	1	B	•	•	↕	↕	⑥	↕
Shift Left, Arithmetic	ASL							68	7	2	78	6	3				M	•	•	↕	↕	⑥	↕
	ASLA													48	2	1	A	•	•	↕	↕	⑥	↕
	ASLB													58	2	1	B	•	•	↕	↕	⑥	↕
Shift Right, Arithmetic	ASR							67	7	2	77	6	3				M	•	•	↕	↕	⑥	↕
	ASRA													47	2	1	A	•	•	↕	↕	⑥	↕
	ASRB													57	2	1	B	•	•	↕	↕	⑥	↕
Shift Right, Logic	LSR							64	7	2	74	6	3				M	•	•	R	↕	⑥	↕
	LSRA													44	2	1	A	•	•	R	↕	⑥	↕
	LSRB													54	2	1	B	•	•	R	↕	⑥	↕
Store Acmltr.	STAA				97	4	2	A7	6	2	B7	5	3				A → M	•	•	↕	↕	R	•
	STAB				D7	4	2	E7	6	2	F7	5	3				B → M	•	•	↕	↕	R	•
Subtract	SUBA	80	2	2	90	3	2	A0	5	2	B0	4	3				A − M → A	•	•	↕	↕	↕	↕
	SUBB	C0	2	2	D0	3	2	E0	5	2	F0	4	3				B − M → B	•	•	↕	↕	↕	↕
Subtract Acmltrs.	SBA													10	2	1	A − B → A	•	•	↕	↕	↕	↕
Subtr. with Carry	SBCA	82	2	2	92	3	2	A2	5	2	B2	4	3				A − M − C → A	•	•	↕	↕	↕	↕
	SBCB	C2	2	2	D2	3	2	E2	5	2	F2	4	3				B − M − C → B	•	•	↕	↕	↕	↕
Transfer Acmltrs	TAB													16	2	1	A → B	•	•	↕	↕	R	•
	TBA													17	2	1	B → A	•	•	↕	↕	R	•
Test, Zero or Minus	TST							6D	7	2	7D	6	3				M − 00	•	•	↕	↕	R	R
	TSTA													40	2	1	A − 00	•	•	↕	↕	R	R
	TSTB													50	2	1	B − 00	•	•	↕	↕	R	R

LEGEND:

OP   Operation Code (Hexadecimal);
~   Number of MPU Cycles;
#   Number of Program Bytes;
+   Arithmetic Plus;
−   Arithmetic Minus;
•   Boolean AND;
M_{SP} Contents of memory location pointed to be Stack Pointer;

+   Boolean Inclusive OR;
⊕   Boolean Exclusive OR:
$\overline{M}$ Complement of M;
→   Transfer Into;
0   Bit = Zero:
00   Byte = Zero;

Note — Accumulator addressing mode instructions are included in the column for IMPLIED addressing

CONDITION CODE SYMBOLS:

H   Half-carry from bit 3;
I   Interrupt mask
N   Negative (sign bit)
Z   Zero (byte)
V   Overflow, 2's complement
C   Carry from bit 7
R   Reset Always
S   Set Always
↕   Test and set if true, cleared otherwise
•   Not Affected

INDEX REGISTER AND STACK MANIPULATION INSTRUCTIONS

		IMMED			DIRECT			INDEX			EXTND			IMPLIED			BOOLEAN/ARITHMETIC OPERATION	COND. CODE REG. 5 H	4 I	3 N	2 Z	1 V	0 C
POINTER OPERATIONS	MNEMONIC	OP	~	#	OP	~	#	OP	~	#	OP	~	#	OP	~	#							
Compare Index Reg	CPX	8C	3	3	9C	4	2	AC	6	2	BC	5	3				$X_H - M, X_L - (M+1)$	•	•	⑦	↕	⑧	•
Decrement Index Reg	DEX													09	4	1	$X - 1 \rightarrow X$	•	•	↕	↕	•	•
Decrement Stack Pntr	DES													34	4	1	$SP - 1 \rightarrow SP$	•	•	•	•	•	•
Increment Index Reg	INX													08	4	1	$X + 1 \rightarrow X$	•	•	•	↕	•	•
Increment Stack Pntr	INS													31	4	1	$SP + 1 \rightarrow SP$	•	•	•	•	•	•
Load Index Reg	LDX	CE	3	3	DE	4	2	EE	6	2	FE	5	3				$M \rightarrow X_H, (M+1) \rightarrow X_L$	•	•	⑨	↕	R	•
Load Stack Pntr	LDS	8E	3	3	9E	4	2	AE	6	2	BE	5	3				$M \rightarrow SP_H, (M+1) \rightarrow SP_L$	•	•	⑨	↕	R	•
Store Index Reg	STX				DF	5	2	EF	7	2	FF	6	3				$X_H \rightarrow M, X_L \rightarrow (M+1)$	•	•	⑨	↕	R	•
Store Stack Pntr	STS				9F	5	2	AF	7	2	BF	6	3				$SP_H \rightarrow M, SP_L \rightarrow (M+1)$	•	•	⑨	↕	R	•
Indx Reg → Stack Pntr	TXS													35	4	1	$X - 1 \rightarrow SP$	•	•	•	•	•	•
Stack Pntr → Indx Reg	TSX													30	4	1	$SP + 1 \rightarrow X$	•	•	•	•	•	•

JUMP AND BRANCH INSTRUCTIONS

OPERATIONS	MNEMONIC	RELATIVE OP	~	#	INDEX OP	~	#	EXTND OP	~	#	IMPLIED OP	~	#	BRANCH TEST	H (5)	I (4)	N (3)	Z (2)	V (1)	C (0)
Branch Always	BRA	20	4	2										None	•	•	•	•	•	•
Branch If Carry Clear	BCC	24	4	2										C = 0	•	•	•	•	•	•
Branch If Carry Set	BCS	25	4	2										C = 1	•	•	•	•	•	•
Branch If = Zero	BEQ	27	4	2										Z = 1	•	•	•	•	•	•
Branch If ≥ Zero	BGE	2C	4	2										$N \oplus V = 0$	•	•	•	•	•	•
Branch If > Zero	BGT	2E	4	2										$Z + (N \oplus V) = 0$	•	•	•	•	•	•
Branch If Higher	BHI	22	4	2										C + Z = 0	•	•	•	•	•	•
Branch If ≤ Zero	BLE	2F	4	2										$Z + (N \oplus V) = 1$	•	•	•	•	•	•
Branch If Lower Or Same	BLS	23	4	2										C + Z = 1	•	•	•	•	•	•
Branch If < Zero	BLT	2D	4	2										$N \oplus V = 1$	•	•	•	•	•	•
Branch If Minus	BMI	2B	4	2										N = 1	•	•	•	•	•	•
Branch If Not Equal Zero	BNE	26	4	2										Z = 0	•	•	•	•	•	•
Branch If Overflow Clear	BVC	28	4	2										V = 0	•	•	•	•	•	•
Branch If Overflow Set	BVS	29	4	2										V = 1	•	•	•	•	•	•
Branch If Plus	BPL	2A	4	2										N = 0	•	•	•	•	•	•
Branch To Subroutine	BSR	8D	8	2											•	•	•	•	•	•
Jump	JMP				6E	4	2	7E	3	3				See Special Operations	•	•	•	•	•	•
Jump To Subroutine	JSR				AD	8	2	BD	9	3					•	•	•	•	•	•
No Operation	NOP										01	2	1	Advances Prog. Cntr. Only	•	•	•	•	•	•
Return From Interrupt	RTI										3B	10	1		•	•	•	•	•	•
Return From Subroutine	RTS										39	5	1		•	•	•	•	•	•
Software Interrupt	SWI										3F	12	1	See Special Operations	•	⑩	•	•	•	•
Wait for Interrupt*	WAI										3E	9	1		•	⑪	•	•	•	•

*WAI puts Address Bus, R/W, and Data Bus in the three-state mode while VMA is held low.

SPECIAL OPERATIONS

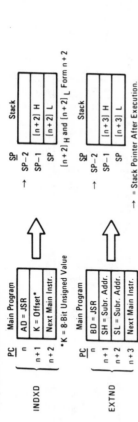

JSR, JUMP TO SUBROUTINE:

INDXD

PC	Main Program
n	AD = JSR
n + 1	K = Offset*
n + 2	Next Main Instr.

	Stack
SP →	
SP − 1	[n + 2] H
SP	[n + 2] L

[n + 2]$_H$ and [n + 2]$_L$ Form n + 2

PC	Subroutine
INX + K	1st Subr. Instr.

*K = 8-Bit Unsigned Value

EXTND

PC	Main Program
n	BD = JSR
n + 1	SH = Subr. Addr.
n + 2	SL = Subr. Addr.
n + 3	Next Main Instr.

	Stack
SP →	
SP − 1	[n + 3] H
SP	[n + 3] L

PC	Subroutine
S	1st Subr. Instr.

(S Formed From S$_H$ and S$_L$)

↑ = Stack Pointer After Execution.

BSR, BRANCH TO SUBROUTINE:

PC	Main Program
n	8D = BSR
n + 1	± K = Offset*
n + 2	Next Main Instr.

	Stack
SP →	
SP − 1	[n + 2] H
SP	[n + 2] L

n + 2 Formed From [n + 2]$_H$ and [n + 2]$_L$

PC	Subroutine
n + 2 ± K	1st Subr. Instr.

*K = 7-Bit Signed Value;

JMP, JUMP:

INDXD

PC	Main Program
n	6E = JMP
n + 1	K = Offset
X + K	Next Instruction

EXTENDED

PC	Main Program
n	7E = JMP
n + 1	K$_H$ = Next Address
n + 2	K$_L$ = Next Address
K	Next Instruction

RTS, RETURN FROM SUBROUTINE:

PC	Subroutine
S	39 = RTS

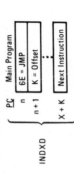

	Stack
SP →	
SP + 1	N$_H$
SP +	N$_L$

PC	Main Program
n	Next Main Instr.

RTI, RETURN FROM INTERRUPT:

Interrupt Program

PC
S | 3B = RTI |

⇑

Main Program

PC
n | Next Main Instr. |

	Stack
SP	
SP + 1	Condition Code
SP + 2	Acmltr B
SP + 3	Acmltr A
SP + 4	Index Register (X_H)
SP + 5	Index Register (X_L)
SP + 6	N_H
→ SP + 7	N_L

CONDITION CODE REGISTER MANIPULATION INSTRUCTIONS

OPERATIONS	MNEMONIC	IMPLIED OP	~	#	BOOLEAN OPERATION	5 H	4 I	3 N	2 Z	1 V	0 C
Clear Carry	CLC	0C	2	1	0 → C	•	•	•	•	•	R
Clear Interrupt Mask	CLI	0E	2	1	0 → I	•	R	•	•	•	•
Clear Overflow	CLV	0A	2	1	0 → V	•	•	•	•	R	•
Set Carry	SEC	0D	2	1	1 → C	•	•	•	•	•	S
Set Interrupt Mask	SEI	0F	2	1	1 → I	•	S	•	•	•	•
Set Overflow	SEV	0B	2	1	1 → V	•	•	•	•	S	•
Acmltr A → CCR	TAP	06	2	1	A → CCR	•	•	•	•	•	• (12)
CCR → Acmltr A	TPA	07	2	1	CCR → A	•	•	•	•	•	•

CONDITION CODE REGISTER NOTES: (Bit set if test is true and cleared otherwise)

1	(Bit V)	Test: Result = 10000000?
2	(Bit C)	Test: Result = 00000000?
3	(Bit C)	Test: Decimal value of most significant BCD Character greater than nine? (Not cleared if previously set.)
4	(Bit V)	Test: Operand = 10000000 prior to execution?
5	(Bit V)	Test: Operand = 01111111 prior to execution?
6	(Bit V)	Test: Set equal to result of N⊕C after shift has occurred.
7	(Bit N)	Test: Sign bit of most significant (MS) byte = 1?
8	(Bit V)	Test: 2's complement overflow from subtraction of MS bytes?
9	(Bit N)	Test: Result less than zero? (Bit 15 = 1)
10	(All)	Load Condition Code Register from Stack. (See Special Operations)
11	(Bit I)	Set when interrupt occurs. If previously set, a Non-Maskable Interrupt is required to exit the wait state.
12	(All)	Set according to the contents of Accumulator A.

PL/F (6800 version)

by F. G. Duncan

Language description

PL/F is a programming language developed for real-time applications on microprocessors. This appendix describes the version for the Motorola 6800 processor. A different version also exists for the Intel 8080 processor.

The philosophy of PL/F is to provide the benefits of a high-level language while preserving the control normally available only at the assembly-language level. The language is suitable for use by both experienced and inexperienced programmers.

1. General layout

A PL/F program consists of declarations and statements, each of which is terminated by a semi-colon. This permits a statement to span more than one line, with the NEWLINE being equivalent to a space. The following symbols are permitted within a PL/F program:

Letters A to Z
Digits 0 to 9
+ − / * % @ ! ( ) , ; : = space ' $ # < > ↑ ←

Any other symbols are flagged as errors, and spaces substituted in their place.

Declarations allow the programmer to control allocation of storage, define simple macros, and define procedures. Procedures are subroutines that are invoked by certain PL/F statements. These procedures may contain further declarations that control storage allocation and define nested procedures. These facilities permit the programmer to breakdown his program into a number of modules, each of which can be written and tested independently of the others. This makes debugging a much simpler task and allows parts of one program to be incorporated into others.

As mentioned above, declarations can handle storage allocation. PL/F has two basic data types: BYTE which is represented by an eight-bit word, and ADDRESS which is represented by two adjacent eight-bit words, giving a 16-bit number (the more significant part of the word is always in the lower address.)

Most statements consist of assigning the value of an expression to a variable. This is called an assignment statement. Other statement types exist to give conditional and unconditional branching, and to give looping facilities.

Any statement can be preceded by one or more labels. A label is an identifier followed by a colon. Some examples are:

X: Y: statement
LAB1:   statement
LABA: LABB: LABC: statement

Labels allow the programmer to refer to the labelled statement from some other point in the program without having to know its address.

This introduction has referred to such terms as identifiers and numbers. These terms and others are defined in the next sections.

2. Identifiers

An identifier in PL/F consists of a letter, optionally followed by any number of digits and letters. Any imbedded $ symbols are transparent. Hence the following are legal identifiers:

X   A17B3   ERRORCOUNT   ERROR$COUNT

Note that the last two examples are treated as the same identifier.

3. Constants

A constant is a sequence of digits. Normally these are to the base 10, but the base can be altered to binary, octal or hexadecimal (hex) by placing the required base letter after the number. The letter codes are as follows:

B   binary, e.g. 10111001B
O, Q octal, e.g. 377Q 1764O
D   decimal, e.g. 989D or 989
H   hex, e.g. 0ABH 9999H 0FFFFH

4. Strings

A string is a sequence of symbols enclosed within primes ('). Any character, including those outside the standard PL/F set, is allowed within strings. To insert a prime in a string, two adjacent primes are used, e.g.

'HERE IS A STRING'
'HERE'' S A STRING'

5. Comments

PL/F allows the programmer to insert comments at any point in the program. These can be inserted in two ways:

(a) Any symbols after a ↑ on the same line will be treated as comment, i.e. ignored by the compiler.
(b) All symbols between and including /* and */ will be treated as comment. This form of comment can appear anywhere a space is valid.

6. Expressions

As stated in a previous section, there are single-length and double-length variables in PL/F. These can be combined within an expression without error, since every combination produces a defined result. An expression consists of variables combined by the various address, arithmetic, logical and relational operators, in accordance with normal algebraic notation, e.g.

$A + B$ $A + B - C$ $A - (B + C) - D$

Operators in expressions have an assumed precedence that determines the order in which they are evaluated. The various PL/F operators are listed below in descending order of precedence. Those on the same level of precedence are strictly evaluated from left to right. The exception to this rule is when two or more monadic operators (single operand) are adjacent to one another (e.g. NOT $-$ A), in which case they are evaluated from right to left.

@
% * } (address operators: see section 25)
ASL ASR ROL ROR LSR NOT $-$ (shifts and 1's and 2's complement)
! (subscript operator: see section 25)

+ − PLUS MINUS   (add and subtract, without and with carry)
= # < > LE GE   (relational operators)
AND   (logical AND)
OR XOR   (logical inclusive and exclusive OR)

Note that the '−' operator occurs twice at different levels of precedence; firstly as a monadic negate, and secondly as a diadic subtract. Hence the expression A OR B AND C − D + E will be evaluated in the order − + AND OR.

Every expression results in either a single-byte or a double-byte result. The following conventions determine which type of result is generated. For convenience, * is used to signify any operator.

(a) BYTE*BYTE always generates a BYTE result.
(b) For logical and arithmetic operators,
     BYTE*ADDRESS
     ADDRESS*ADDRESS } always generate an ADDRESS result.
     ADDRESS*BYTE
     The more significant byte, where necessary, is padded with zeroes.
(c) Relational operators always generate a BYTE result; if result is true, all bits are set to one, i.e. 0FFH; if result is false, result is zero.
(d) A string with one symbol is treated as an eight-bit constant with a value equal to the ASCII code for that symbol; the parity bit can be specified by the programmer in any of the four possible ways (see page 187). A string with two symbols will be treated as a 16-bit number; the first symbol will form the less significant byte. Longer strings will be truncated to the first two symbols. For example, 'A' is equal to 0C1H, 'AC' is equal to 0C3C1H.

Variables in an expression can take any of the following forms:

(a) An identifier that has been declared as BYTE or ADDRESS. The value of the variable is the contents of the store location to which it refers.
(b) An identifier that has been previously set up as a label. Its value is a constant equivalent to the address to which the label points.
(c) A constant.
(d) A string − see note (d) above.
(e) A procedure call that returns a value (see section 18).
(f) The identifier PC. This is a 16-bit constant whose value is the address at the beginning of the current statement.

The programmer must be careful when mixing BYTE and ADDRESS variables in an expression. When a BYTE is expanded to ADDRESS size, the top byte is zero-filled.

e.g. Z is an address variable with value −1 (FFFF), I is a byte variable with value −1 (FF), then I + Z gives result FFFF + 00FF = 00FE

A procedure that converts an eight-bit signed number to a 16-bit signed number is:

```
SIGNEXT: PROC (X) ADDRESS;
    DEC (X, I, J) BYTE;
    J: = X;
    IF X GE 0 THEN I:= 0; ELSE I:= 0FFH;
    RETURN *@I;
    END SIGNEXT;
```

Then SIGNEXT (I) + Z = FFFF + FFFF = FFFE.

7. Assignment statements

An assignment statement is one in which the value of an expression is stored in one or more locations. The general form of an assignment statement is as follows:

Variable   Assignment operator   Expression

The assignment operator can be either:= or ←.

The variable must be an identifier that has been previously declared as either BYTE or ADDRESS, or a legal address expression (see section 25, address operators). The variable can be a variable list, in which case the value of the expression is assigned to each of the variables listed. The variables must be separated by commas. For example:

```
A: = B + C;
VARA:= VARB OR VARC + (A = B);
A, B, C, D, E:= 0;
```

If the expression value is of type BYTE and the assignment variable is of type ADDRESS, the more significant byte will be set to zero. Similarly, if the expression is of type ADDRESS and the assignment variable is of type BYTE, the top byte of the result is ignored.

8. Declarations

The declaration of variables and macros is made by the DECLARE statement. The general form of this statement is as follows:

DECLARE or DEC   variable list   length   type   value;

The variable list can be one or more identifiers. If only one is required, the identifier name only is required. However, if more than one is required, the names must be separated by commas, and the whole list enclosed in round brackets. For example:

DEC VAR BYTE:
DECLARE (VARA, VARB, VARC) ADDRESS;

The normal length of a variable is one, in which case the length need not be specified. However, the programmer frequently needs to set up a table or array where he only wishes to give the first element an identifier. The length of this table is expressed as a constant enclosed within round brackets.

DECLARE TABLE (20) BYTE;
DEC ARRAY (100Q) ADDRESS;

In the first example, 20 consecutive locations are reserved, and the identifier TABLE refers to the first of these. In the second case, 128 (100Q = 64D) consecutive locations are reserved. This is because 64 units of type ADDRESS have been requested and each one takes up two bytes, giving a total of $64 \times 2 = 128$.

When the length part is omitted, either one or two locations are reserved, depending on whether BYTE or ADDRESS is used. Here are some more examples:

DECLARE (A, B, C, D) (4) ADDRESS;   uses 32 locations
DEC (X, Y, Z) BYTE;   uses 3 locations

More than one declaration can be made in the same statement. Each declaration is simply separated by commas:

DECLARE (COUNT, I) BYTE, POINTERS (20) ADDRESS;

Consecutive declarations use consecutive locations in store. Hence, in the above example, I is in the next location to COUNT, POINTERS is in two locations after COUNT, and the next declaration will start 40 locations after POINTERS.

When a label is referenced in an INITIAL list (see section 9), it must first be explicitly declared before it is defined by a statement alongside it. This is done by using the type word LABEL in a declare statement. Labels cannot be initialised, nor can they have other than unit length. Some examples are:

DEC (M0, M1, M2) LABEL;
DECLARE LAB LABEL;

9. Initial values

All variables declared are initialised to zero, unless otherwise indicated. This can be done by using the INITIAL attribute in the DECLARE statement. It comes at the end of the statement immediately after the type word, and takes the form of the word INITIAL followed by a list of initialisation values, which can be strings, constants, variables, procedures, and labels. The values are assigned to the variables in the order in which they are declared, until either the variable space or the constants are exhausted. For example:

DECLARE (A, B, C, D, E, F) BYTE INITIAL (1, 2, 3, 4, 5, 6);
DEC TABLE (6) ADDRESS INITIAL (1, 2, 3, 4, 5, 6);

The first example sets A to 1, B to 2, C to 3, etc. The second sets the first pair of locations to 1, the second pair to 2, etc.

When strings are used in INITIAL lists, each symbol in the string is assigned to the next byte, whether it is part of an ADDRESS or BYTE variable. When the end of the string is reached, the next value will always go to the next whole variable. For example:

DEC (TAB1, TAB2) (8) BYTE INITIAL ('STRING1', 'STRING2');

The first string exactly fits the first table, but the last byte of the second will need to be filled with zero.

DECLARE (A, B, C, D) ADDRESS INITIAL ('ABCDEFGH');

Variable A will have the symbols AB, B will have CD, etc.

10. Macros

Macros are used to associate a string with an identifier. This association takes place at compile time, so that the compiler actually sees the string rather than the identifier. A macro definition takes the form:

DECLARE identifier LITERALLY string;

The contractions LIT and AS can be used for the more cumbersome LITERALLY. Macro definitions can themselves contain macro calls, as long as they do not exceed a depth of five and are not recursive. Examples are:

DECLARE TRUE AS '377Q', FALSE AS '0';
DEC FOREVER AS 'WHILE TRUE';

11. Conditional statements

The general format of this statement is as follows:

IF condition THEN statement 1; ELSE statement 2;

The condition can be any expression, and the value of it is tested for being non-zero (non-zero in PL/F is assumed as being true). Hence, if the expression has a non-zero value, statement 1 is obeyed. The ELSE part is optional, but if it is present, statement 2 is obeyed. The statements after the THEN and ELSE can themselves be conditional statements. To avoid conflicting THENs conflicting with a solitary ELSE, it is defined that the ELSE always goes with the nearest THEN. For example:

IF A = B THEN IF A LE B THEN A:= B; ELSE A:= B + 1;

Here, the ELSE applies to the second THEN.

12. Do statements

Often the programmer wants to place more than one statement after a THEN or ELSE. This is done by surrounding the group of statements by two other short statements; a DO at the beginning, and an END at the end. The resultant group can be placed anywhere a single statement is valid. For example:

IF A = B THEN DO; A:= A − 1; B:= B + 1; END;
IF A LE B THEN A:= C; ELSE DO; A:= A − 1; C:= 0; END;

13. Do while statements

Another useful facility is to be able to repeatedly obey a group of statements while some condition holds. The form of this statement in PL/F is:

DO WHILE condition is true; statements; END;

Unlike the IF statement, the DO and the END are always present, whether there is one or more statements in the repeat part. Section 17 shows some extensions to this statement type. Some examples are:

DO WHILE A GE B; A:= A − 1; C:= C + 1; END;
DO WHILE 1; A:= A + 1; END;

DEC FOREVER AS 'WHILE 1';
DO FOREVER; A:= A + 1; END;

14. Goto statements

The GOTO statement permits the programmer to transfer control from the GOTO statement to some other specified point in the program. The general form of it is:

GOTO destination;

The destination can be any of the following:
(a) A label that is declared somewhere else in the program. The label can be declared either before or after the GOTO statement.
(b) A constant, specifying an absolute address within the machine.
(c) An expression enclosed in round brackets. The value of the expression determines the address to which control is passed.

Some examples are:

GOTO L1;   GOTO 770;   GOTO (JMPTAB!A);

Although no error will be indicated, it is advisable not to jump outside the current block, particularly if inside a procedure. This point is more fully explained in section 24. The use of GOTOs should be avoided altogether whenever possible. The word GOTO can be written as two separate words GO and TO.

15. Halt statement

This statement inserts a wait instruction in the code, which effects the suspension of the program until an interrupt is received. It is simply written as:

HALT;

16. End of source statement

The last statement in a PL/F program should be EOF. This tells the compiler that there is no more input to come. However, it is normally possible to omit this statement, although such practice is not recommended.

17. Extensions to statement types

Any expression in PL/F can be preceded by a DO ... END or a DO
WHILE ... END group of statements. This allows a number of other
statement types to be constructed. For instance, it is often very useful
to place the condition of a DO WHILE ... END group other than at
the start. The following definitions achieve this:

DEC NDO AS 'DO WHILE DO;' ; NWHILE AS 'END;';

Then one can write:

NDO statements; NWHILE expression; statements; END;

Other statements could be similarly constructed.

18. Procedures

Procedures are subroutines that are invoked by certain PL/F statements.
However, they must be declared before they can be invoked. A procedure can optionally have values passed to it on invocation (parameters),
and optionally return a value to the point of invocation (this type is
called a function). Parameters are included in the procedure declaration,
and the values supplied at the point of invocation can be referred to by
the parameter names within the procedure body. Parameters are always
called by value.

   Functions, i.e. procedures that return a value, are invoked differently
from those that do not.

19. Procedure declaration

The general form of a procedure declaration is:

name: PROCEDURE   parameter list   procedure value   type;

PROC can be used instead of PROCEDURE. The name of the procedure is any identifier that has not been used for another purpose. The
parameter list is optional and is a number of identifiers, separated by
commas, and enclosed in round brackets. The procedure value is also
optional and indicates the value returned by the procedure (if any). This
is simply the word BYTE or ADDRESS. When parameters are used,
their types must be declared immediately afterwards by a DECLARE
statement. They do not have to be declared in the same order as they

appear in the procedure declaration, and can also be intermingled with other variable declarations. The compiler restricts the programmer to a maximum of two parameters.

The last statement in every procedure must be an END statement. The END must also be followed by the procedure name, to distinguish a procedure from a DO statement and from other procedures. This ensures that nested procedures are terminated in the correct sequence. For example:

```
ADD: PROC (X, Y) BYTE;
     DEC (I, Y, X) BYTE;
     statements;
     END ADD;
```

20. Returning from procedure to point of invocation

This is performed by the RETURN statement. When the procedure is due to return a value, the word RETURN must be followed by an expression, which is the value to be returned. For example:

```
ADD:    PROC (X, Y) BYTE;
        DEC (X, Y, I) BYTE;
        RETURN X+Y;
        END ADD;
```

21. Procedure invocation

As indicated previously, a procedure can be invoked in two ways, depending on whether it generates a value or not. For a procedure that returns a value (a function), it is invoked from within an expression. For example:

```
A: = ADD (A, B);
```

This calls the procedure declared in the last section, and the values of A and B are placed in X and Y respectively. Thus the procedure actually returns the value of A + B and assigns it to A. This is equivalent to writing A: = A + B;

Where a procedure does not return any value, it cannot be invoked from within an expression. Instead, it requires its own statement type. This is done by putting CALL in front of the normal procedure name and parameters. For example:

CALL TEST;

A procedure that returns a value but has no parameters must still have the brackets after it, even though there is nothing enclosed by them. This condition does not apply to CALL statements. For example:

TEST1: PROC BYTE; RETURN 24; END TEST1;
A:= TEST1 ( ) ;   but not   A:= TEST1;

22. Linking-in external machine-code segments

In a real-time environment, there are some tasks that are better written directly in machine code or assembly language, due to time constraints. PL/F allows the programmer to interface segments of machine code to his PL/F program.

It actually provides two alternative methods of doing this, depending on whether the machine code is to be included within the PL/F program. If the code is short, it can be put in a DECLARE statement with an INITIAL list containing the required instructions. If the code is longer, only its start address need be supplied, and the code can be loaded separately from the PL/F program. The following examples explain the linkage mechanism.

(a) Code included within program:

DEC SHIFTCODE (4) BYTE INITIAL (226Q, 300Q, 110Q, 71Q);
SHIFT: PROC (X) BYTE EXTERNAL SHIFTCODE;
    DEC (X) BYTE; END SHIFT;

The instructions are:

LDA A, DIR (300Q)
ASL A
RTS

(b) Code not in program:

SHIFT: PROC (X) BYTE EXTERNAL 5703Q;
    DEC X BYTE; END SHIFT;

In general, therefore, the start address of a procedure can be specified explicitly as either a constant or a variable. This is done by placing an EXTERNAL attribute on the procedure declaration.

A table of parameter addresses is printed at the end of the source listing to allow these machine-code segments to access parameters. If the procedure returns a value, this is returned in the accumulators. For a BYTE result, it is returned in the A accumulator. For an ADDRESS result, the less significant byte is returned in the A accumulator, and the more significant part in the B accumulator.

23. Interrupt procedures

PL/F allows the programmer to invoke a procedure from an external interrupt. However, an interrupt procedure cannot have any parameters or return a value. There are three interrupt vectors in the Motorola 6800: RST (reset), MSK (maskable), and NMI (non-maskable). A procedure can be linked to any one of these three by placing the INTERRUPT attribute on the procedure declaration. This attribute comes between the value type and EXTERNAL attributes. The word INTERRUPT is followed by the channel name, i.e. RST, MSK or NMI. The compiler prints a table of vector addresses at the end of the listing. For example:

TTIN: PROC INTERRUPT MSK;

An interrupt procedure can be invoked from within a PL/F program, assuming only one procedure is used. This is necessary since the SWI interrupt vector, like the others, will normally be in ROM and hence cannot be dynamically altered by program. The procedure is invoked by a normal call statement, and a SWI instruction will be generated. The SWI vector will be printed at the end, showing the required entry address.

If, at run time, no MSK interrupt is used, a SEI instruction is obeyed, otherwise a CLI instruction is used.

24. Block structure

PL/F is a block-structured language. This means that the scope of each variable need not be the entire program. (The *scope* of a variable is the region of a program in which it can be used.) The block level is altered by various PL/F statements. It is increased within a procedure body and within a DO or a DO WHILE group. It is decreased by any END statement. Hence the parameters and any other variables declared within a procedure cease to exist after the end of the procedure declaration. The names can therefore be used again. However, unlike some languages, each identifier name can be used only once at any point in the program.

Once the block level has decreased past the level at which any variable was declared, that variable no longer exists. This does not apply to labels and procedures, which remain global to the whole program, irrespective of the level at which they were declared.

Jumping explictly from a block can lead to hidden complications. Normally, it is acceptable to jump from a DO WHILE block, as long as a procedure boundary is not crossed. Jumping outside a procedure is highly dangerous, since this leaves the return address on the stack. Procedures should always be terminated by the RETURN statement.

The listing generated by the PL/F compiler shows the block level outstanding at the end of each source line. A maximum of nine block levels (from 1 to 9) is permitted by the compiler. For example:

```
1    DEC (A, B, C, D) BYTE;
2    PROC1: PROC (X, Y) BYTE;
2        DEC (X, Y, TEMP) BYTE;
2        TEMP:= X + Y; RETURN TEMP − A;
1    END PROC1;
1    A:= B + C + PROC1 (C, D);
```

In the above example, A, B, C and D are valid throughout. X, Y and TEMP are valid only within the procedure. Another example is:

```
1    DECLARE (A, B, C) BYTE, (X, Y, Z) ADDRESS;
2    T1: PROC (M, N);
2        DECLARE (M, N, O) BYTE;
2        . . .
1    END T1;
2    T2: PROC (M, N);
2        DEC (M, N, O) ADDRESS;
3        T3: PROC (P, Q) BYTE;
3            DEC (P, Q, R) ADDRESS;
3            . . .
2        END T3;
2        . . .
1    END T2;
1    . . .
```

25. Address operators

PL/F contains three types of address operators. Their significance, although at first perhaps not obvious, is explained by examples as follows.

(a) *The @ operator.* This operator, when placed in front of a variable name, gives a constant, which is the address of that variable. Normally it generates a 16-bit constant, unless the variable is in the base page. For example:

DEC (X, Y) ADDRESS;
X:= @ Y;

The above statement puts the address of Y in the locations X and X + 1. This value is actually the address of the more significant byte of variable Y. @ (Y + 1) would give the address of the less significant byte.

(b) *The * and % operators.* These two operators are the inverse of the @ operator. When placed in front of an expression, they cause the value of an expression to be treated as an address: % treats the resultant address as a BYTE variable, and * treats it as an ADDRESS variable. These operators can appear on both sides of an assignment statement. For example:

X:= * (X + 10);
*X:= Y;

In the first example, the contents of locations X + 11 and X + 10 are assigned to X + 1 and X. In the second example X and X + 1 specify the destination address. (X is the more significant part, X + 1 is the less significant part.)

By combining the @ and type (b) operators, two interesting effects can be obtained:

- Coercing from byte to address and vice versa. If X is of mode BYTE, and Y is of mode ADDRESS, *@X makes X appear as though it were declared as mode ADDRESS. Similarly, %@Y causes the more significant word of Y to be treated as a BYTE variable; % (@Y + 1) coerces the less significant word of Y to BYTE.
- Passing parameters by reference. The following example illustrates how the addresses of variables can be passed over to a procedure to effect call by reference. The example is equivalent to the statement B:= A + B;

```
T1:   PROC (X, Y);
      DEC (X, Y) ADDRESS;
      %Y:= %Y + %X;
END T1;
DEC (A, B) BYTE;
A, B:= 20;
CALL T1 (@A, @B);
```

(c) *The subscript operators* ! *and* !!. These are both mapped into a sequence of other operations. The indirection operator outside the brackets is dependent on the mode of the operand on the left-hand side of the ! or !!. The ! maps as follows:

DEC (X, Y) ADDRESS, (I, J) BYTE;
X!I is equivalent to *(@X + I)
I!J is equivalent to %(@I + J)

X!!I is equivalent to *(X + I)
I!!J is equivalent to %(I + J)

Hence the first element of a table has subscript zero and subsequent bytes go up in steps of 1. In the above example, Y equals X!2, J equals X!5, and J also equals I!1. Obviously, I equals I!0. The subscript operator can take any sub-expression as subscript, but the subscripted variable must obey the same rules as the @ operator (this applies to ! only). For address variables, remember that the subscript rises in steps of 2, since the subscript is simply an address offset from the subscripted location. Also note that X!0 is the more significant part, X!1 the less significant part.

Multiple indirection is not implemented in the compiler; if required, it should be effected by repeated assignments.

26. Inline code

Inline instructions and operands can be inserted among PL/F statements. There are three possibilities, as follows.

INST = CODE, value;

This inserts the instruction with op-code 'value' in the code area; 'value' must be a constant.

INST = BYTE, operand;

This inserts 'operand' in the code area as an eight-bit (one-word) operand; 'operand' can be a constant, a label, a variable or a procedure. In the last three cases, the bottom eight bits of address are inserted as operand.

INST = ADDRESS, operand;

This inserts 'operand' in the code area as a 16-bit (two-word) operand; 'operand' is as for BYTE, except that the full 16 bits of an address are used.

Compiler controls

1. Store address allocation

With microprocessors, it is essential that a high-level language cope with mixtures of memory types (e.g. ROM, RAM, base page) and non-continuous address maps. PL/F has a number of variable and code areas, at present four for each of code and variables. Each area can be initialised to a given base address, and the area currently in use can be switched at any stage. The areas into which code and variables are compiled are entirely independent, and hence switching the area of one does not affect the other. Each area has a default base address, which normally can be overwritten only before that area is actually used. Also, once an area has been used, it cannot normally be re-initialised. These two restrictions can be lifted from each area by 'unprotecting' it. The base address is always the lowest, since locations are allocated in ascending order. The above is performed by the following statements:

(a) Selecting an area:

   GLOBS = A1;
   GLOBS = A2;
   GLOBS = A3;
   GLOBS = A4;
   CODE = A1;
   CODE = A2;
   CODE = A3;
   CODE = A4;

(b) Initialising an area:

   GLOBS = A1, constant;
   GLOBS = A2, constant;
   GLOBS = A3, constant;
   GLOBS = A4, constant;
   CODE = A1, constant;
   CODE = A2, constant;
   CODE = A3, constant;
   CODE = A4, constant;

(c) Unprotecting an area:

   GLOBS = A1, UNPROTECT;
   GLOBS = A2, UNPROTECT;
   GLOBS = A3, UNPROTECT;
   GLOBS = A4, UNPROTECT;

```
CODE = A1, UNPROTECT;
CODE = A2, UNPROTECT;
CODE = A3, UNPROTECT;
CODE = A4, UNPROTECT;
```

A1 for code is not related in any way to A1 for globals. The default start area for both code and variables is A1. Note that the area-initialisation statement and the unprotect statement do not select the area to which they refer.

2. Main/secondary segments

The compiler can optionally generate extra code to initialise the microprocessor at the start of the program. This involves loading stack pointer register (SP), setting or clearing the interrupt mask, and placing the entry address on a start block on paper tape output. This can only be specified before any code is generated from a PL/F program, hence it is advisable to place it at the start of the input stream. Default assumes MAIN status. The statement is:

```
SEG = MAIN;
SEG = SUB;
```

3. Stack pointer value

As explained above, the SP is initialised at the top of the main segment. The programmer would normally wish to allocate his own space to the stack, so an initialisation statement is provided to do this. If a value is provided before any code is generated, that value is used in the MAIN segment initialisation code. If it appears at a later stage, a new SP load instruction is generated. The statement form is:

```
STACK = constant;
```

4. Parity

The parity bit on characters in the input stream is automatically handled by the compiler. The parity bit of each symbol in compiler strings can be set to any of the four possible combinations by the following statement. The default value is SET.

PARITY = EVEN;
PARITY = ODD;
PARITY = SET;
PARITY = UNSET;

5. Listing control

The compiler can optionally generate a number of listings, each of which can be switched on and off as often as required. The following listings are available, and are all produced by default.

(a) *Source listing.* This gives each source statement accompanied by its number, block level, and any errors. Each time it is switched on, a new page and heading are given. At the end of input, if LIST is currently on, a printout of compiler dictionary, interrupt and parameter addresses, and code and global area boundary addresses, is also printed. The form of this switch statement is:

LIST = ON;
LIST = OFF;

(b) *Generated code listing.* Selected parts of the generated code can also be listed. This is produced after the source has been read, and all the (a) listings have been produced. It provides a reverse-assembled layout of the generated instructions and operands, giving associated source line numbers and accumulative instruction-execution times. Instruction, address and operand values are normally printed in octal, but can be converted to hexadecimal by the BASE command. These commands are as follows:

CDLIST = ON;
CDLIST = OFF;
BASE = 16;
BASE = 8;

6. Source control

PL/F is designed to run on a file-store oriented operating system. On entering the compiler, the input file name is picked up and input is then taken from that file. The method of picking up this name is system dependent and hence is explained on page 191. Files can be substituted into the main file, nested to a maximum of six levels. When the end of a substitution file is reached, the compiler reverts to the file it was in when the substitution command was encountered, at the point at which it left off. If the main file reaches the end without an EOF being encountered, an EOF statement is assumed. Due to differing formats in system file names, the name is supplied as a string. The form of substitution command is:

SRC = 'file name';

7. Parameter storage area

Parameters in PL/F are allocated absolute locations in memory. The base of this area can be located anywhere in store, and so a statement is provided to initialise it. The default value of 140 (octal) is assumed if the statement is not present. The statement form is:

PARMS = constant;

8. Temporary variable space

As with parameters, a fixed area of store is allocated for use by expressions. This defaults to 0, but can be set elsewhere by the following statement. The address must be in the bottom 32K. The statement form is:

TEMPS = constant;

Implementation features

1. Parameter handling

The 6800 compiler allocates locations in memory for parameters. These locations are printed out in a table at the end of the listing of the source program; the range of these parameters is also given at the end of the dictionary listing. The start address of this area can be set by the user (see above).

2. Returning procedure values

A BYTE result is returned in the A accumulator. An ADDRESS result is returned with the less significant word in the A accumulator, and the more significant word in the B accumulator.

3. Temporary expression results

In evaluating expressions, it is often necessary to store sub-expression results in temporary locations. Although the same locations can be used over and over in the same procedure, once the procedure is terminated, those locations are frozen for further use. This prevents a location being overwritten by a function call in the middle of an expression. The limits of this area are printed at the bottom of the dictionary listing. The start address of this area can be set by the user, but defaults to address 0. It is strongly recommended that this area be situated in the base page, since this considerably increases the resultant code's execution speed.

4. Interrupts

A table of values is printed corresponding to the interrupt vectors in the top four pairs of locations in the 6800 address space. These are the entry addresses of these interrupt types. If no RST procedure is present, the normal program start address is printed instead.

Error codes

A   Illegal operand for the @ operator.
B   Illegal base for a constant.
C   Wrong number of parameters.
D   Illegal digit in number.
E   Error in DECLARE statement.
F   Full dictionary.
G   Bad procedure type declaration.
H   Too many block levels.
I   Illegal character.
J   Compiler control statement error.
K   Assignment statement error.
L   String is too long.
M   Too many items in list.
N   No procedure name to match declaration.
O   Error in GOTO statement.
P   Bad parameter list.
Q   Error in parameter.
R   Error in RETURN statement.
S   Illegal statement type.
T   Line too long; truncated to fit listing, input unaffected.
U   Undefined identifier.

V Too many levels of substitution of macros.
W Wrong sequence of procedure ENDs.
X Syntax error in expression.
Y Reverse polish stack overflow.
Z String table part of dictionary full.
≠ Procedure table full.
$ Parameter area full.
% Temporary locations area full.

Using RT-11 system on the PDP-11

In the following commands, the underlined characters are the machine output. The rest is typed by the user. All input lines are terminated by a carriage return. The upper-case words denote system names, while lower-case denotes user-supplied names.

<u>.</u> R STAB
<u>*</u> FD1MP1.PLF/C
<u>**</u> Source, output, listing, printer-width

source	input file name (must be supplied)
output	intermediate file name (defaults to PLFTMP.PS1)
listing	source listing device or file (defaults to errors only on TT:)
printer-width	number of columns on listing device (defaults to 80 columns)

If no errors are detected in the first pass, the system continues as follows:

<u>**</u> Input, tape, listing

input	output file from first pass (defaults to PLFTMP.PS1)
tape	output device or file for generated code (defaults to no output)
listing	listing device or file for dictionary and code listings (defaults to no listing, but if switch-on encountered with default condition, then LP: assumed)

Paper tape format

The 6800 compiler generates a paper tape of generated code and globals in the standard MIKBUG loader format. For those having to supply their own load software, the format is briefly described.

The information is split into a series of blocks, with each block containing a variable number of consecutive location values. Each block has a warning character, a block type character, a block size count, block start address, data values, and finally a checksum character. With the exception of the first two items, each eight-bit value is coded as two hexadecimal digits, with the more significant four bits first. With the load address, the more significant eight bits come first.

The count value is the number of eight-bit units of data plus the offset 3.

The warning character is always an S. The block types are as follows:

(a) *Data block*. The type is indicated by a 1 following the S. The data is loaded into the address given on block.

(b) *Start block*. Indicated by a 9 after the S. The loader should execute a jump to the address given on tape.

The loader should add the binary value of each eight-bit byte value read together, ignoring overflow. When the checksum at the end of the block is also added, the resultant value should come to 255, i.e. all 1's.

Blocks can be immediately adjacent to one another. However, to improve legibility, the compiler inserts a carriage return and line feed at the end of each block, followed by some blank frames.

PL/F sample program

This is the PL/F equivalent of the teletype exchange program discussed in chapter 8. The listing shows the source program, details of procedures and variables, and the machine code generated by the compiler.

```
001 1
002 1
003 1
004 1    * TELETYPE EXCHANGE PROGRAM - PL/F VERSION
005 1
006 1    * FIRST DECLARE ADDRESSES, CONSTANTS AND ARRAYS
007 1
008 1    CODE = A1,2000H;                  *CODE TO GO TO 2000 HEX
009 1    GLOBS = A1,100H;                  *GLOBAL VARIABLES TO GO TO 100H
010 1
011 1    DECLARE TLINE AS '%0F100H' ;*ADDRESS OF FIRST TERMINAL LINE
012 1    DECLARE CLINE AS '%0F200H'; *ADDRESS OF FIRST COMPUTER LINE
013 1    DECLARE TR(20) BYTE;             *ARRAY TR (20 ELEMENTS )
014 1    DECLARE LR(5) BYTE ;             *ARRAY LR (5 ELEMENTS
015 1    DECLARE BELL AS '7';
016 1    BASE=16;                         *ENSURES PROGRAM DUMP IN HEX
017 1
018 1    *NOW SUBROUTINES, IN THE REVERSE ORDER TO CHAPTER 8
019 1
020 2    LSERVE: PROC (X);                *SERVICE LINE X
021 2       DEC (X,D,F,Y) BYTE;
022 2       Y:=ASL(ASL X);
023 2       IF CLINE!(3+Y) =0 THEN RETURN; *OUT IF NO CHARACTER READY
024 2       D:=CLINE!(2+Y);               *GET CHARACTER
025 3          IF LR!X GE 0 THEN DO; *IF LINE ALLOCATED
026 3          F:=LR!X;                   *GET TERMINAL NUMBER
027 3          TLINE!(ASL( ASL F)) :=D; *AND SEND CHARACTER TO TERMINAL
028 2             END;
029 2       RETURN;
030 1    END LSERVE;
031 1
032 2    LINESCAN: PROC;·                 *CHECKS 5 COMPUTER LINES IN SEQUENCE
033 2       DEC A BYTE;
034 2       A:=0;
035 3       DO WHILE A#5;
036 3          CALL LSERVE(A);           *CALL LSERVE WITH PARAMETER A
037 3          A:=A+1;
038 2       END;
039 2       RETURN;
040 1    END LINESCAN;
041 1
042 2    YN:PROC (X,Y);   *PASS CHARACTER Y
043 2                     * ON COMPUTER LINE ALLOCATED TO TERMINAL X
044 2       DEC(X,Y,Z) BYTE;
045 2       Z:=TR!X;
046 2       CLINE!(ASL( ASL Z)) :=Y;
047 2       RETURN;
048 1    END YN;
049 1
050 1
051 2    NN:PROC(X,Y) ;   *TRY TO ALLOCATE A LINE TO TERMINAL X
052 2       DEC (X,Y,P) BYTE;
053 2       P:=0;         *LOOK FOR A FREE COMPUTER LINE
054 2       DO WHILE P#5 OR LR!P#0FFH; P:=P+1; END;
055 3       IF P=5 THEN DO; *LINE NOT FOUND
056 3          TLINE!(ASL( ASL X)):=BELL; *SEND BELL
057 3          RETURN;
058 2          END;
```

```
59 2      LRIPI:=X; TRIX:=P;*LINE FOUND, ASSIGN POINTERS
60 2      CALL YN(X,Y);        *SEND CHARACTER
61 2      RETURN;
62 1 END NN;
63 1
64 2 YY:PROC (X);             *DEALLOCATE LINE FROM TERMINAL X
65 2      DEC (X,Y) BYTE;
66 2      Y:=TRIX;
67 2      TRIX:=0FFH;
68 2      LRIY:=0FFH;
69 2      RETURN;
70 1 END YY;
71 1
72 1
73 2 TSERVE: PROC (X) ;       *PROCEDURE TO SERVICE TERMINAL X
74 2      DEC(X,D) BYTE;      *X IS PARAMETER GIVING TERMINAL NUMBER. D IS
75 2                         * A LOCAL VARIABLE TO GIVE TEMPORARY
76 2                         *STORAGE TO A NEW CHARACTER
77 2      IF TLINEI(3+ ASL( ASL X)) =0   *CHECK LINE STATUS REGISTER
78 2            THEN RETURN;             *OUT IF NO CHARACTER READY
79 2      D:=TLINEI(2+ASL( ASL X));      *OTHERWISE GET NEW CHARACTERD
80 2                                     *AND STORE IN D
81 2      IF TRIX GE 0 THEN              *TEST IF COMPUTER LINE ALLOCATED
82 2         IF D= BELL THEN  CALL YY(X);*CALL YY IF CHAR IS BELL
83 2            ELSE CALL YN(X,D);       *OR YN IF CHAR NOT BELL
84 2            ELSE                     *IF LINE NOT ALLOCATED
85 2         IF D#BELL THEN CALL NN(X,D); *CALL NN IF CHAR NOT BELL
86 2      RETURN;
87 1 END TSERVE;
88 1
89 2 KBSCAN: PROC;            *CHECKS 20 TERMINAL LINES IN SEQUENCE
90 2      DEC A BYTE;         *A IS A LOCAL VARIABLE
91 2         A:=0;
92 3         DO WHILE A # 20;
93 3            CALL TSERVE(A);*CALL TSERVE WITH PARAMETER A
94 3            A:=A+1;
95 3         END;
96 2      RETURN;
97 1 END KBSCAN;
98 1
99 2 BEGIN:PROC;             *TOP SUBROUTINE IN HIERARCHY
00 2      DEC P BYTE;
01 2      P:= 0;             *SET ALL ELEMENTS OF TR TO -1
02 2      DO WHILE P#20; TRIP:=0FFH; P:=P+1; END;
03 2      P:=0;
04 2      DO WHILE P#5; LRIP := 0FFH; P:=P+1; END;
05 3      DO WHILE 1;    *CALL KBSCAN AND LINFSCANE CONTINUOUSLY
06 3         CALL KBSCAN;
07 3         CALL LINFSCAN;
08 2      END;
09 1 END BEGIN;
10 1
11 1 * AND NOW, FINALLY ,
12 1
13 1 CALL BEGIN;
14 1 EOF;
```

    NO ERRORS IN PROGRAM

PROCEDURE TABLE

PROCEDURE		PARAMETER 1		PARAMETER 2		RESULT
PROCEDURE	LSERVE	BYTE	60			
PROCEDURE	LINESCAN					
PROCEDURE	YN	BYTE	61	BYTE	62	
PROCEDURE	NN	BYTE	63	BYTE	64	
PROCEDURE	YY	BYTE	65			
PROCEDURE	TSERVE	BYTE	66			
PROCEDURE	KBSCAN					
PROCEDURE	BEGIN					

INTERRUPT VECTORS

MASKABLE	0
SWI	0
NMI	0
RESET	2000

DICTIONARY CONTENTS

NAME	TYPE	VALUE
TR	BYTE	100
LR	BYTE	114
LSERVE	PROCEDURE	2007
LINESCAN	PROCEDURE	2076
YN	PROCEDURE	2094
NN	PROCEDURE	20BC
YY	PROCEDURE	2144
TSERVE	PROCEDURE	217B
KBSCAN	PROCEDURE	21EE
BEGIN	PROCEDURE	220C

GLOBAL AREA 1 FROM 100 TO 122

CODE AREA 1 FROM 2000 TO 2267

TEMPORARY VARIABLES FROM 0 TO C

PARAMETER AREA FROM 60 TO 66

NE NUMBER	CYCLE COUNT	ADDRESS	OP. CODE	MNEMONIC	OPERAND
20	3	2000	8E	LDS #	200
	5	2003	E	CLI	
	5	2004	2	NOP	
	8	2004	7E	JMP EXT	2264
22 LSERVE:	11	2007	96	LDA A,DIR	X
	13	2009	48	ASL A	
	15	200A	48	ASL A	
	20	200B	B7	STA A,EXT	Y
23	22	200E	86	LDA A,#	3
	26	2010	BB	ADD A,EXT	Y
	28	2013	8B	ADD A,#	0
	30	2015	C6	LDA B,#	F2
	32	2017	C9	ADC B,#	0
	36	2019	97	STA A,DIR	1
	40	201B	D7	STA B,DIR	0
	44	201D	DE	LDX DIR	0
	51	201F	6D	TST IND	0
	55	2021	26	BNE	1
	60	2023	39	RTS	
24	62	2024	86	LDA A,#	2
	66	2026	BB	ADD A,EXT	Y
	68	2029	8B	ADD A,#	0
	70	202B	C6	LDA B,#	F2
	72	202D	C9	ADC B,#	0
	76	202F	D7	STA B,DIR	0
	80	2031	97	STA A,DIR	1
	84	2033	DE	LDX DIR	0
	89	2035	A6	LDA A,IND	0
	94	2037	B7	STA A,EXT	D
25	96	203A	86	LDA A,#	14
	99	203C	9B	ADD A,DIR	X
	101	203E	C6	LDA B,#	1
	103	2040	C9	ADC B,#	0
	107	2042	97	STA A,DIR	1
	111	2044	D7	STA B,DIR	0
	115	2046	DE	LDX DIR	0
	122	2048	6D	TST IND	0
	126	204A	2D	BLT	29
26	128	204C	86	LDA A,#	14
	131	204E	9B	ADD A,DIR	X
	133	2050	C6	LDA B,#	1
	135	2052	C9	ADC B,#	0
	139	2054	D7	STA B,DIR	0
	143	2056	97	STA A,DIR	1
	147	2058	DE	LDX DIR	0
	152	205A	A6	LDA A,IND	0
	157	205C	B7	STA A,EXT	F

27					
	161	205F	B6	LDA A,EXT	F
	163	2062	48	ASL A	
	165	2063	48	ASL A	
	167	2064	8B	ADD A,#	0
	169	2066	C6	LDA B,#	F1
	171	2068	C9	ADC B,#	0
	175	206A	D7	STA B,DIR	0
	179	206C	97	STA A,DIR	1
	183	206E	B6	LDA A,EXT	D
	187	2071	DE	LDX DIR	0
	193	2073	A7	STA A,IND	0

29	198	2075	39	RTS	

32

34 LINESCAN:	200	2076	4F	CLR A	
	205	2077	B7	STA A,EXT	A

35	209	207A	B6	LDA A,EXT	A
	211	207D	81	CMP A,#	5
	215	207F	27	BEQ	12

36	219	2081	B6	LDA A,EXT	A
	223	2084	97	STA A,DIR	60
	232	2086	BD	JSR EXT	LSERVE

37	236	2089	B6	LDA A,EXT	A
	238	208C	4C	INC A	
	243	208D	B7	STA A,EXT	A

38	246	2090	7E	JMP EXT	207A

39	251	2093	39	RTS	

42

45 YN:	253	2094	4F	CLR A	
	256	2095	9B	ADD A,DIR	X
	258	2097	C6	LDA B,#	1
	260	2099	C9	ADC B,#	0
	264	209B	D7	STA B,DIR	2
	268	209D	97	STA A,DIR	3
	272	209F	DE	LDX DIR	2
	277	20A1	A6	LDA A,IND	0
	282	20A3	B7	STA A,EXT	Z

46	286	20A6	B6	LDA A,EXT	Z
	288	20A9	48	ASL A	
	290	20AA	48	ASL A	
	292	20AB	8B	ADD A,#	0
	294	20AD	C6	LDA B,#	F2
	296	20AF	C9	ADC B,#	0
	300	20B1	D7	STA B,DIR	2
	304	20B3	97	STA A,DIR	3
	307	20B5	96	LDA A,DIR	Y
	311	20B7	DE	LDX DIR	2
	317	20B9	A7	STA A,IND	0

47	322	20BB	39	RTS	

51

53 NN:	324	20BC	4F	CLR A	
	329	20BD	B7	STA A,EXT	P
54	333	20C0	86	LDA A,EXT	P
	335	20C3	81	CMP A,#	5
	339	20C5	27	BEQ	4
	341	20C7	86	LDA A,#	FF
	345	20C9	20	BRA	1
	347	20CB	4F	CLR A	
	349	20CC	C6	LDA B,#	14
	353	20CE	FB	ADD B,EXT	P
	357	20D1	97	STA A,DIR	4
	359	20D3	86	LDA A,#	1
	361	20D5	89	ADC A,#	0
	365	20D7	D7	STA B,DIR	6
	369	20D9	97	STA A,DIR	5
	373	20DB	DE	LDX DIR	5
	378	20DD	A6	LDA A,IND	0
	380	20DF	81	CMP A,#	FF
	384	20E1	27	BEQ	4
	386	20E3	86	LDA A,#	FF
	390	20E5	20	BRA	1
	392	20E7	4F	CLR A	
	395	20E8	9A	ORA A,DIR	4
	397	20EA	4D	TST A	
	401	20EB	27	BEQ	A
	405	20ED	B6	LDA A,EXT	P
	407	20F0	4C	INC A	
	412	20F1	B7	STA A,EXT	P
	415	20F4	7E	JMP EXT	20C0
55	419	20F7	B6	LDA A,EXT	P
	421	20FA	81	CMP A,#	5
	425	20FC	26	BNE	15
56	428	20FE	96	LDA A,DIR	X
	430	2100	48	ASL A	
	432	2101	48	ASL A	
	434	2102	8B	ADD A,#	0
	436	2104	C6	LDA B,#	F1
	438	2106	C9	ADC B,#	0
	442	2108	D7	STA B,DIR	4
	446	210A	97	STA A,DIR	5
	448	210C	86	LDA A,#	7
	452	210E	DE	LDX DIR	4
	458	2110	A7	STA A,IND	0
57	463	2112	39	RTS	
59	465	2113	86	LDA A,#	14
	469	2115	BB	ADD A,EXT	P
	471	2118	C6	LDA B,#	1
	473	211A	C9	ADC B,#	0
	477	211C	D7	STA B,DIR	4
	481	211E	97	STA A,DIR	5
	484	2120	96	LDA A,DIR	X
	488	2122	DE	LDX DIR	4
	494	2124	A7	STA A,IND	0
	496	2126	4F	CLR A	
	499	2127	9B	ADD A,DIR	X
	501	2129	C6	LDA B,#	1
	503	212B	C9	ADC B,#	0
	507	212D	D7	STA B,DIR	4
	511	212F	97	STA A,DIR	5
	515	2131	B6	LDA A,EXT	P
	519	2134	DE	LDX DIR	4
	525	2136	A7	STA A,IND	0

60	528	2138	96	LDA A,DIR	X
	532	213A	97	STA A,DIR	61
	535	213C	96	LDA A,DIR	Y
	539	213F	97	STA A,DIR	62
	548	2140	BD	JSR EXT	YN
61	553	2143	39	RTS	
64					
66 YY:	555	2144	4F	CLR A	
	558	2145	9B	ADD A,DIR	X
	560	2147	C6	LDA B,#	1
	562	2149	C9	ADC B,#	0
	566	214B	D7	STA B,DIR	7
	570	214D	97	STA A,DIR	8
	574	214F	DE	LDX DIR	7
	579	2151	A6	LDA A,IND	0
	584	2153	B7	STA A,FXT	Y
67	586	2156	4F	CLR A	
	589	2157	9B	ADD A,DIR	X
	591	2159	C6	LDA B,#	1
	593	215B	C9	ADC B,#	0
	597	215D	D7	STA B,DIR	7
	601	215F	97	STA A,DIR	8
	603	2161	86	LDA A,#	FF
	607	2163	DE	LDX DIR	7
	613	2165	A7	STA A,IND	0
68	615	2167	86	LDA A,#	14
	619	2169	BB	ADD A,EXT	Y
	621	216C	C6	LDA B,#	1
	623	216E	C9	ADC B,#	0
	627	2170	D7	STA B,DIR	7
	631	2172	97	STA A,DIR	8
	633	2174	86	LDA A,#	FF
	637	2176	DE	LDX DIR	7
	643	2178	A7	STA A,IND	0
69	648	217A	39	RTS	
73					
77 TSERVE:	651	217B	96	LDA A,DIR	X
	653	217D	48	ASL A	
	655	217E	48	ASL A	
	657	217F	8B	ADD A,#	3
	659	2181	8B	ADD A,#	0
	661	2183	C6	LDA B,#	F1
	663	2185	C9	ADC B,#	0
78	667	2187	97	STA A,DIR	A
	671	2189	D7	STA B,DIR	9
	675	218B	DE	LDX DIR	9
	682	218D	6D	TST IND	0
	686	218F	26	BNE	1
	691	2191	39	RTS	

79	694	2192	96	LDA A,DIR	X
	696	2194	48	ASL A	
	698	2195	48	ASL A	
	700	2196	8B	ADD A,#	2
	702	2198	8B	ADD A,#	0
	704	219A	C6	LDA B,#	F1
	706	219C	C9	ADC B,#	0
	710	219E	D7	STA B,DIR	9
	714	21A0	97	STA A,DIR	A
	718	21A2	DE	LDX DIR	9
	723	21A4	A6	LDA A,IND	0
	728	21A6	B7	STA A,EXT	D
81	730	21A9	4F	CLR A	
	733	21AA	9B	ADD A,DIR	X
	735	21AC	C6	LDA B,#	1
	737	21AE	C9	ADC B,#	0
	741	21B0	97	STA A,DIR	A
	745	21B2	D7	STA B,DIR	9
	749	21B4	DE	LDX DIR	9
	756	21B6	6D	TST IND	0
	760	21B8	2D	BLT	20
82	764	21BA	B6	LDA A,EXT	D
	766	21BD	81	CMP A,#	7
	770	21BF	26	BNE	A
	773	21C1	96	LDA A,DIR	X
	777	21C3	97	STA A,DIR	65
	786	21C5	BD	JSR EXT	YY
83	789	21C8	7E	JMP EXT	21D7
	792	21CB	96	LDA A,DIR	X
	796	21CD	97	STA A,DIR	61
	800	21CF	B6	LDA A,EXT	D
	804	21D2	97	STA A,DIR	62
	813	21D4	BD	JSR EXT	YN
84	816	21D7	7E	JMP EXT	21ED
85	820	21DA	B6	LDA A,EXT	D
	822	21DD	81	CMP A,#	7
	826	21DF	27	BEQ	C
	829	21E1	96	LDA A,DIR	X
	833	21E3	97	STA A,DIR	63
	837	21E5	B6	LDA A,EXT	D
	841	21E8	97	STA A,DIR	64
	850	21EA	BD	JSR EXT	NN
86	855	21ED	39	RTS	
89					
91 KBSCAN:	857	21EE	4F	CLR A	
	862	21EF	B7	STA A,EXT	A
92	866	21F2	B6	LDA A,EXT	A
	868	21F5	81	CMP A,#	14
	872	21F7	27	BEQ	12
93	876	21F9	B6	LDA A,EXT	A
	880	21FC	97	STA A,DIR	66
	889	21FE	BD	JSR EXT	TSERVE

94		893	2201	B6	LDA A,FXT	A
		895	2204	4C	INC A	
		900	2205	B7	STA A,EXT	A
95		903	2208	7E	JMP EXT	21F2
96		908	220B	39	RTS	
99						
101	BEGIN:	910	220C	4F	CLR A	
		915	220D	B7	STA A,EXT	P
102		919	2210	B6	LDA A,EXT	P
		921	2213	81	CMP A,#	14
		925	2215	27	BEQ	1C
		927	2217	4F	CLR A	
		931	2218	BB	ADD A,EXT	P
		933	221B	C6	LDA B,#	1
		935	221D	C9	ADC B,#	0
		939	221F	D7	STA B,DIR	B
		943	2221	97	STA A,DIR	C
		945	2223	86	LDA A,#	FF
		949	2225	DE	LDX DIR	B
		955	2227	A7	STA A,IND	0
		959	2229	B6	LDA A,FXT	P
		961	222C	4C	INC A	
		966	222D	B7	STA A,EXT	P
		969	2230	7E	JMP EXT	2210
103		971	2233	4F	CLR A	
		976	2234	B7	STA A,FXT	P
104		980	2237	B6	LDA A,EXT	P
		982	223A	81	CMP A,#	5
		986	223C	27	BEQ	1D
		988	223E	86	LDA A,#	14
		992	2240	BB	ADD A,EXT	P
		994	2243	C6	LDA B,#	1
		996	2245	C9	ADC B,#	0
		1000	2247	D7	STA B,DIR	B
		1004	2249	97	STA A,DIR	C
		1006	224B	86	LDA A,#	FF
		1010	224D	DE	LDX DIR	B
		1016	224F	A7	STA A,IND	0
		1020	2251	B6	LDA A,EXT	P
		1022	2254	4C	INC A	
		1027	2255	B7	STA A,EXT	P
		1030	2258	7E	JMP EXT	2237
106		1039	225B	BD	JSR EXT	KBSCAN
107		1048	225E	BD	JSR EXT	LINESCAN
108		1051	2261	7E	JMP EXT	225B
113		1060	2264	BD	JSR EXT	BEGIN
114		1069	2267	3E	WAI	
		1071	2003	F	SFI	

Index

203

microprocessors
and microsystems

*the authoritative international journal
on microcomputer technology and
applications for designers*

Ten issues a year from January 1979

Further details and subscription rates from: David Burt,
IPC Science and Technology Press Ltd, Westbury House,
Bury Street, Guildford, Surrey GU2 5AW England
Telephone: (0483) 31261 Telex: 859556 Scitec G